Maths. Pyramid

TEACHER'S BOOK 3

Contents

Introduction ii

Framework for Teaching Mathematics Planning Grids iv

Units 1 to 35 2

Photocopy Masters 72

National Numeracy Strategy Teaching Objectives 109

Match to Published Maths Schemes 112

Match to Northern Ireland Lines of Development 117

Match to Scotland 5–14 Guidelines 118

Answers to Pupil's Book questions 121

Introduction

Maths Pyramid

Maths Pyramid is designed to complement your main maths teaching resource by providing further, more in-depth work within each topic. Because the National Numeracy Strategy places such great emphasis on keeping the children together on each topic, it is important to ensure that brighter children are able to fulfil their potential in a whole-class context. Maths Pyramid provides the perfect solution to this problem. Matched not only to the Framework for Teaching Mathematics, Scotland 5–14 Guidelines and Northern Ireland Lines of Development, but also to a range of whole-school maths programmes, Maths Pyramid is the only comprehensive teaching resource to be produced specifically with more-able children in mind. The units are ordered according to the Framework for Teaching Mathematics planning grid, and are written specifically to allow children who have quickly achieved the day's (or week's) teaching objectives further to extend their mathematical knowledge. Our aim is to encourage children to develop a good understanding of mathematics, to enjoy thinking mathematically, and to investigate mathematical issues with confidence and enthusiasm.

Planning and classroom management

The scheme is planned for the more able pupils in each class. It provides an instant resource for differentiated group work with these pupils, providing lessons with a good level of challenge.

The work is organised to meet the needs of each age group and this affects the classroom organisation and management required. Pupils need to explore mathematical concepts through practical tasks and within their play, with plenty of opportunities given to consolidate their learning.

Teaching Maths Pyramid

Each unit of Maths Pyramid covers approximately a week's teaching. To this end, there are typically five structured teaching inputs in each unit, containing an oral introduction, one or more activities to extend the children's knowledge of the topic area, and some suggested discussion points. Maths Pyramid is written to allow maximum flexibility, so in each unit there are inputs requiring different levels of involvement from the teacher. Each input is readily adaptable for group, individual or whole class work with a top set. The inputs are laid out as opposite.

Assumed Classroom Materials

- number cards (0 to 30)
- number line, graded in halves
- interlocking cubes (for example Multilink or Unifix)
- building materials (LEGO, Poleidoblocs and so on)
- dominoes (sets are assumed to be complete)
- playing cards (sets are assumed to be complete)
- counters (several colours)
- dice (spotted, 1 to 6 and 1 to 9)
- calculators
- coins and notes (real and plastic)
- sets of plastic 2D and 3D shapes (different colours, shapes and materials)
- containers (for work with capacity using sand or water)
- pegboard, pegs and elastic bands
- hoops (for sets work)
- Blu-tack or similar
- stopwatch or timer
- geared analogue clock with moveable hands
- digital clock
- weighing balances/scales
- rice, sand or pulses (for work with weight)
- set of weights
- measuring equipment (rulers, tape measures, metre sticks)
- selection of packets and bottles (for work with measures)
- Base ten equipment
- counting materials (buttons, marbles and so on)
- demonstration calendar
- mirrors (for work with line symmetry)
- matchsticks or lolly sticks

Each unit title lays out the topics covered, exactly matching the Framework for Teaching Mathematics. A brief introductory section gives you more precise detail on the teaching content of the unit.

Some activities would benefit from the assistance of an adult, for example where all the children are putting number cards in order.

This type of activity, typically written with a group of three or four children in mind, forms the core of Maths Pyramid. The children, once the rules of the game or practical activity have been explained, can be left to get on with their work.

Most activities are prefaced by a brief oral introduction or guided introductory exercise led by the teacher. This section can be shortened or extended as appropriate to teaching a top set or a small group within a class.

These activities are more investigative, and may be extended over the course of the week or involve an element of homework. The children, once they have been introduced to the terms of the investigation, work alone or in pairs on an 'open-ended' activity. The children might need general supervision, but should not require detailed guidance.

UNIT 11

Understanding +, −, Time including Problems, Making Decisions and Checking Results

This week we are working on investigations, patterns and understanding of addition and subtraction and solving problems.

OBJECTIVES
- To use knowledge that addition can be done in any order to do mental calculations more efficiently.
- To use known number facts to add and subtract mentally.
- To read and begin to write the vocabulary related to time.

LANGUAGE
horizontal, vertical, diagonal • digital, analogue

RESOURCES
PCM 13, analogue and digital clocks, timers (1-minute and 10-minute) square dotted paper.

Teaching Input 1

- Add together 115 + 225 + 35. How did you work it out?
- Add 95 + 63. How did you calculate it?
- What is 230 − 30 and 650 − 230? How do you know?
- Which three numbers will make 50 when added together? What about 90 or 150?
- How many do you add to 40 to make 100? 150? 67?
- What is the total of 12 + 15? Of 12 + 17 + 10?
- How many more than 5 are 49 and 50?
Repeat each question format several times.
- Can each of you, in turn, ask the group a sum using + and −?

Adult supervision recommended
Draw the following diagram on the board:

- Add each pair of neighbouring numbers. (2 + 3 = 5, 3 + 4 = 7, 4 + 5 = 9, 5 + 6 = 11, 6 + 2 = 8.)

22

- Now add all these totals together. What do you get?
- Change the position of some numbers to try and make higher and lower totals. What do you discover?
Change the arrangement but keep the same numbers.

- What have you found out? Can you explain your work?
- Could you make or find a rule?

Teaching Input 2

- Add 16 + 12 + 5 + 4.
- Add 18 + 10 + 12.
- What about 18 + 12 + 10?
- How many hundreds, tens and units are there in 216? 314? 462? 814? 330 and 951?
Repeat several times.
- What do you do when you add 63 + 29? 14 + 23? 140 + 800?
- What is 192 + 6? 752 + 2? 769 + 5? 80 + 25? 60 + 76? 45 + 23?
Repeat several times.
- What do you add to 992 to reach 1000? To get from 998 to 1000? To get from 1000 to 1009?
Repeat several times.

UNDERSTANDING +, −, TIME INCLUDING PROBLEMS, MAKING DECISIONS AND CHECKING RESULTS **UNIT 11**

PCM 13
Ask the children to complete the PCM by following the instructions above each arrow.

- Can you describe what you have been doing? Can you see a pattern?

Teaching Input 3

analogue and digital clocks
- How many seconds are there in a minute?
- How many minutes are there in an hour?
- How many hours are there in a day?
Show the children the analogue clock and ask them to read the time – quarter past, half past, quarter to, 6 o'clock, 9 o'clock and 12 o'clock. Then ask them to read 5 past 6, ten past 6, quarter past 6, twenty minutes past 6 and half past 6.
Now look at a digital clock, asking the children to read 6:05, 6:20 and 6:15.
Compare analogue and digital times and repeat the exercise with other times.

1-minute and 10-minute timers
Draw the following table on the board and ask the children to copy it into their books.

What I can do in 1 minute	What I can do in 10 minutes	What I can do in 1 hour

Encourage them to find things to do and check if their estimates were correct by using a 1-minute and 10-minute timer.

- Discuss what you can do in 1 minute. Did anyone do anything different? Did the time pass quickly? Were any of your guesses wildly wrong?

Teaching Input 4

- How long does it take to drink a glass of water?
- How long does it take to watch a film?
- How long does it take to eat lunch?
- How long do you think playtime is?
- How long are you at school?
- How long do you sleep at night?

square dotted paper
Draw the following on the board before playing 'Squares' in pairs.

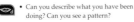

Ask the children, in their pairs, to copy the diagram on square dotted paper.
Players take it in turns to draw a line, either vertical or horizontal, joining two adjacent dots. The player who completes a box scores the number in that box and also has a second turn. When there are no more spare lines, the scores are all added up; the highest score wins.

- What numbers did you get? What totals?
- Did anyone get a higher total? What numbers did you have?
- What was the smallest total? Which numbers did you have?
- Did anyone get a different total? Which numbers added up to that total?

Teaching Input 5

- What is double 5? Double 6? Double 7? Double 8? Double 9? Double 10? Double 20?
- What is double 50? Double 25? Double 100? Double 200 and 250?
- What is half of 16? Of 18? 20, 12 and 14?
- What is 2 × 5? 5 × 2? 2 × 6? 6 × 2? 10 × 2? 10 × 5?

- Ask the children to choose any five numbers in the range 1 to 9.
- How many different sums can you make with these numbers using the operations +, −, ×, ÷ and =? Try making all the totals to 50.

- How many different totals did you make? What is the highest and the lowest total? Have you made the same total using different methods? Have you made all the totals up to 50? Which could you not make?

23

Teaching objectives, closely following and extending the objectives laid out by the National Numeracy Strategy, are listed at the head of each unit. A list of important mathematical language to be introduced or reinforced is also included.

Resources for the whole unit are indicated at the head of the page, and individual teaching inputs also carry an indication of necessary materials for quick reference. Photocopy Masters are provided in a bank at the back of the book.

There are frequent suggestions for discussion points following on from teaching inputs or individual activities, from which the teacher may select as appropriate. If a whole class or set is being taught, this section would be appropriate for use in the plenary part of the lesson.

This sort of activity is the most easy for the teacher to manage as it requires a minimum of input – the emphasis is on the children working on their own or in pairs, often from Photocopy Masters. This sort of activity will usually be a follow-up to more detailed teaching input, and should allow children to explore mathematical concepts on their own, or to practise previously-taught skills.

Framework for Teaching Mathematics Planning Grid

Week	Autumn	Spring	Summer
1	**Unit 1 – Place value and ordering (3 days)** To read and write whole numbers to at least 1000 in figures and words and know what each digit represents. To order whole numbers to at least 1000. To count on or back in hundreds. To compare two given 3-digit numbers, say which is more or less and give a number which lies between them.	**Unit 13 – Place value, ordering, estimating and rounding (3 days)** To know what each digit represents and partition numbers. To compare two given 3-digit numbers, say which is more or less and give a number which lies between them.	**Unit 24 – Place value, ordering and rounding (3 days)** To round numbers to the nearest 10. To order whole numbers in words and figures. To read the vocabulary of comparing and ordering numbers. To identify which of a given set of numbers is nearest to another given number.
2	**Unit 2 – Understanding + and − , mental calculation strategies (5 days)** Extend understanding of the operations of addition and subtraction and that more than two numbers can be added. Read and begin to write the vocabulary of addition. To use known number facts and place value to add/subtract mentally. To use the +, − and = signs.	**Unit 14 – Understanding + and −, mental calculation strategies (5 days)** To extend understanding that subtraction is the inverse of addition. To read and begin to write the vocabulary of subtraction. To add or subtract mentally a 'near multiple of 10' to or from a 2-digit number. To use patterns of similar calculations. To bridge through a multiple of 10, then adjust.	**Unit 25 – Understanding + and −, mental calculation strategies (5 days)** To know and use addition and subtraction facts for each number to 20. To use informal pencil and paper procedures to add large sets of numbers. To identify doubles and near doubles of numbers up to 1000.
3	**Unit 3 – Money and 'real life' problems, making decisions, checking results (5 days)** To choose and use appropriate operations (including × and ÷). To solve problems involving numbers in 'real life'. To use doubling or halving, starting from known facts.	**Unit 15 – Money and 'real life' problems, making decisions, checking results (5 days)** To solve word problems involving numbers in real life using one or more steps. To use £.p notation and convert from pence to pounds and vice versa.	**Unit 26 – Money and 'real life' problems (5 days)** To use pencil and paper procedures to solve real life problems with more than one step. To use all four operations in the context of money.
4	**Unit 4 – Measures, including problems (5 days)** To read scales to the nearest division. To measure and compare using standard units To use record estimates and measurements to the nearest whole or half unit or in mixed units. To suggest suitable units and measuring equipment. To use units of time and know the relationship between them.	**Unit 16 – Measures and time, including problems (5 days)** To solve word problems involving measures. To use a ruler to measure lines to the nearest half centimetre. To record estimates and measurements to the nearest whole or half unit and check the accuracy of estimates. To suggest suitable units for all measuring activities. To read accurately analogue and digital clocks.	**Unit 27 – Measures, including problems (5 days)** To solve problems involving measures. To use a range of measuring equipment and read scales accurately to the nearest division. To record estimates and measures in mixed units. To compare measurements and estimates. To use the relationships between units of time.
5	**Unit 5 – Shape and space (4 days)** To classify and describe 2D and 3D shapes according to their properties. To make and describe shapes and patterns, identify and sketch lines of symmetry in simple shapes and recognise shapes with no lines of symmetry.	**Unit 17 – Shape and space (3 days)** To describe and classify 2D and 3D shapes according to their properties. To make and describe 3D shapes. To identify right angles in 2D shapes and in the environment. To understand angle as a measure of turn.	**Unit 28 – Shape and space (4 days)** To use mathematical terms to identify and describe 2D and 3D shapes. To make and describe right-angled turns. To describe and find positions on a grid. To know and use the four compass directions.
6	**Unit 6 – Reasoning about shapes (4 days)** To solve mathematical problems or puzzles, explain methods and discuss reasoning. To recognise simple patterns and relationships.	**Unit 18 – Reasoning about shapes and space (5 days)** To recognise line symmetry. To identify and sketch symmetrical patterns.	**Unit 29 – Reasoning (4 days)** To solve mathematical puzzles and carry out investigations requiring a methodical approach. To explain methods of calculation. To recognise patterns and relationships and ask questions.
7	**Assess and review (2 days)**	**Assess and review (2 days)**	**Assess and review (2 days)**
8	**Unit 7 – Counting and properties of number, reasoning about numbers (5 days)** To solve mathematical problems and explain methods. To recognise familiar multiples. To investigate general statements about familiar numbers. To describe and extend number sequences. To count on or back in a variety of ways.	**Unit 19 – Counting and properties of number, reasoning about numbers (5 days)** To count on or back in tens and hundreds from any 2- or 3- digit number. To recognise odd and even numbers to 100. To investigate patterns and relationships, generalise, predict and explain.	**Unit 30 – Counting and properties of number, reasoning about numbers (5 days)** To recognise and extend number sequences and patterns . To complete sequences with 'missing' numbers. To count on or back in steps of various sizes from any 3-digit number. To recognise 2- and 3-digit multiples of 2, 5 and 10.

Week	Autumn	Spring	Summer
9	**Unit 8 – Understanding ×, ÷, mental calculation strategies (5 days)** To know by heart multiplication facts for the 2, 5 and 10 times-tables. To understand multiplication as repeated addition and extend understanding that it can be done in any order. To understand division as grouping. To use known number facts to carry out mentally simple multiplication or division.	**Unit 20 – Understanding + and −, mental calculation strategies (5 days)** To add three 2-digit numbers. To use knowledge that numbers can be added in any order to do mental calculations more efficiently. To find, describe and use patterns of similar calculations. To extend understanding that subtraction is the inverse of addition.	**Unit 31 – Understanding ×, ÷, mental calculation strategies (5 days)** To recognise that division is the inverse of multiplication and halving is the inverse of doubling. To find remainders after simple division. To check results with an equivalent calculation.
10	**Unit 9 – Money and 'real life' problems, making decisions, checking results (5 days)** To solve problems involving numbers and money. To explain methods orally and in writing. To understand and use £.p notation.	**Unit 21 – Understanding ×, ÷, money and 'real life' problems (5 days)** To recognise all coins, find totals and give change. To use all four operations as appropriate to solve real life problems. To extend understanding that multiplication can be done in any order. To understand that division is the inverse of multiplication.	**Unit 32 – Money and 'real life' problems, making decisions, checking results (5 days)** To solve more complex real life problems using appropriate operations, check results and explain how the problem was solved.
11	**Unit 10 – Fractions (5 days)** To recognise unit fractions and use them to find fractions of shapes and numbers. To begin to recognise simple fractions that are several parts of a whole. To begin to recognise simple equivalent fractions.	**Unit 22 – Fractions (5 days)** To recognise and find simple fractions of shapes and numbers. To create models illustrating simple fractions. To compare simple fractions and order them. To position fractions on a number line.	**Unit 33 – Fractions (5 days)** To find simple fractions of whole numbers up to 20. To recognise patterns in fractions of odd and even numbers. To find equivalents of non-unit fractions. To begin to use fractions in real life problems.
12	**Unit 11 – Understanding +, −, time, including problems, making decisions, checking results (5 days)** To use known number facts to add and subtract mentally. To use knowledge that addition can be done in any order to do mental calculations more efficiently. To read and begin to write the vocabulary related to time.	**Unit 23 – Handling data (5 days)** To collect and sort information and display it in lists and Venn and Carroll diagrams. To interpret the diagrams, answer questions and make statements using them.	**Unit 34 – Understanding + and −, paper and pencil procedures and problems, including time (5 days)** To use number patterns, mental strategies and rapid recall of number facts to perform mental calculations in an efficient manner. To read and interpret timetables. To construct a timeline and to be aware of the passage of time.
13	**Unit 12 – Handling data (5 days)** To use Venn and Carroll diagrams to organise and interpret data.	**Assess and review (2 days)**	**Unit 35 – Data (5 days)** To collect data with the purpose of testing a hypothesis. To represent data in lists, charts, Venn and Carroll diagrams and bar charts. To use the displays to draw conclusions. To consider extensions and the possible wider uses of information.
14	**Assess and review (2 days)**		**Assess and review (2 days)**

Place Value and Ordering

This week we are going to describe and extend number sequences and read and write numbers to 1000, knowing what each digit represents.

OBJECTIVES

- To read and write whole numbers in figures and words to at least 1000.
- To know what each digit represents.
- To order whole numbers to at least 1000.
- To count on or back in hundreds.
- To compare two given three-digit numbers.

LANGUAGE

digits, odd, even • between • hundreds, tens, units, nearest 10, nearest 100

RESOURCES

number cards (1 to 9), PCM 1, Pupils' Book page 1.

Teaching Input 1

- How many pennies are there in £1?
- How many pennies are there in £1.25?
- How many pounds are there in 300 pence?
- How many pounds are there in 368 pence?
- What is 372 pence in pounds and pennies?
- What is the value of each digit in the number 432? *400, 30 and 2.*
- Now what about 378? Or 500? Or 723?
- What do I add to 300 to make 368?
- What do I add to 250 to make 310?
- Which odd numbers lie between 216 and 222?

Repeat using different numbers.

- Which even numbers lie between 531 and 539?

Repeat using different numbers.

number cards (1 to 9)

Adult supervision recommended

Using three sets of number cards, shuffle them together. Ask each child to take three cards and to make the largest number they can with them.

The first child then places their cards face up on the table and says the number they have made. The second child puts their cards above the first number (if it is higher) or below it (if it is lower), as appropriate, and says the number they have

made. Continue until all the children have put their cards in order. Then encourage the group to check that the numbers are in numerical order, and to rearrange them if they are not. When all the cards have been ordered, ask the children to tell you what each digit represents, for example, 931 is 'nine hundred and thirty-one' or 'nine hundreds, three tens and one unit'.

Repeat the activity, this time making the smallest number possible.

Teaching Input 2

- Which number is 10 more than 99? Than 147? Than 263?
- Which number is 100 more than 300? Than 250? Then 370?
- Which number is 100 less than 500? Than 770? Than 990?
- Continue the pattern 80, 90, 100 ... to 150, and back.
- Continue the pattern 200, 250, 300 ... to 500, and back.
- What is 66 rounded to the nearest 10? And 72? 48? 55? 91? 87? 35? 46? 99?

Repeat with other numbers.

- How does this number pattern continue 34, 39, 44 ...?
- Can you continue the sequence 26, 34, 42 ...?
- What about the sequence 95, 100, 105 ... ?

PCM 1

The children complete the PCM by writing in either the figures or the words for the numbers given on the number snakes.

• Could you complete all the number snakes? Were there any you found more difficult? Which did you find easiest?

Teaching Input 3

• What do the digits represent in 430? In 452? In 330? In 409?

• Which number is equivalent to 6 hundreds, 5 tens and 1 unit?

• Which number is equivalent to 7 hundreds, 3 tens and 6 units?

• What about 8 hundreds, 9 tens and 5 units?

• Now tell me what 5 hundreds, 7 tens and 3 units means.

• Which is more: 919 or 991?

• Is 342 more or less than 324? *Write the numbers on the board.*

• Which is more: 314 or 341?

• If my book costs between £2 and £3, what might it cost?

• Now count on in hundreds from 0 to 1000 and back.

• This time count on in tens from 880 to 1000 and back.

Pupils' Book page 1

Ask the children to complete the exercise on Pupils' Book page 1. They must order the first two sets from the largest to the smallest, and write the largest number in words, then order the last two sets from the smallest to the largest, and write the smallest number in words.

• Did you find any of the numbers difficult to order? Which was your largest number? Which was your smallest? How many hundreds, tens and units does each number have?

Understanding + and −, Mental Calculation Strategies

This week we are going to work further on addition and subtraction. We will be extending our understanding that addition can be done in any order, and we will be investigating numbers.

OBJECTIVES

- To extend understanding of the operations of addition and subtraction.
- To extend understanding that more than two numbers can be added.
- To use known number facts and place value to add or subtract mentally.
- To use the +, − and = signs.

LANGUAGE

add, subtract, plus, add on, combinations, total • vertical, horizontal, diagonal • consecutive, pattern • formulae, operation, rules, solution

RESOURCES

Pupils' Book pages 2 and 3, interlocking cubes, PCM 2.

Teaching Input 1

- What is 14 add 10? What about 60 + 13? And 50 + 50? Or 76 + 9? Or 82 + 9? How did you work them out?
- If I think of a number and add 12, the answer is 36. What is my number?
- If I think of a number and add 15, the answer is 45. What is my number?
- Which three numbers added together make 30? Are there any other combinations?
- Add 90 + 23. How did you work it out?
- What is 58 + 62? How did you find the answer?
- Does it matter in which order you add the numbers? How can we make it easier?
- Add 15 + 7 + 15 + 2.
- What is 6 plus 5 plus 10?
- What is 15 − 7? What about 15 − 9? And 15 − 10?
- What is 25 − 7? And 25 − 9? And 25 − 10? Can you see a pattern?

Pupils' Book pages 2 and 3

Ask the children to complete the exercise on Pupils' Book pages 2 and 3, making sure they record every route. When they have finished the activity, encourage them to check their results with a partner – one as A and one as B – by comparing their end totals.

- What was your highest total? What was your lowest total?
- Did A eat the same number of flowers as B?
- What totals did you get between the highest and lowest?
- Did anyone find different routes with the same total?

Teaching Input 2

- Subtract 40 from 65. Now try 60 from 90. And 100 from 250. What about 150 from 300?
- How did you work them all out? Can you tell me a way to check if your answers are correct? Is there another way? *If the children struggle, suggest 65 − 40 = 25, which can be checked by 25 + 40 = 65.*
- What is 18 − 10? And 13 − 6? And 100 − 50? What about 100 − 75? Or 100 − 25? Now try 50p − 10p. What is 500p − 100p? And 550 − 50? And 550 − 500?
- What are the doubles of 7, 9, 11… to 25?
- What are the doubles of 6, 8, 10… to 30?
- Add 55 + 16. How did you work it out?
- Add 64 + 15. How did you do it?
- What is 503 − 500? And 504 − 498? How did you work them out? Did you go back or count on?

Tell the children that numbers can be written as the sum of consecutive numbers, for example, $6 + 7 = 13$ and $5 + 6 + 7 = 18$. Point out, also, that the result number may have more than one combination, for example, 54 can be made from $2 + 3 + 4 + 5 + 6 + 7 + 8 + 9 + 10$ as well as $12 + 13 + 14 + 15$.

Ask the children to investigate which numbers can be written as the sum of consecutive numbers and which cannot. (It is impossible to make the powers of 2 (2, 4, 8, 16, 32 … .)) Then ask them to find numbers that can be made more than one way – can they make all the numbers from 1 to 100?

- Can you see any patterns? Did you have a system for working out the combinations?

Teaching Input 3

- What is $41 + 39$? And $60 + 80$? And $37 + 36$? $26 + 25$? How did you work them out?
- What about $88 − 49$? Or $67 − 51$?
- Can you continue the pattern:
  $5 + 3 = 8$, $15 + 3 = 18$, $25 + 3 = 28$?
- What is $45 + 3$? $55 + 3$? $85 + 3$? $105 + 3$?
- What is $115 − 4$? And $788 − 6$? And $519 − 8$? And $729 + 1$? $264 + 5$? $300 + 37$? $500 + 93$?

interlocking cubes, PCM 2

Ask the children to fill in the numbers on PCM 2, either by totalling the hexagon corner numbers to find the centre number or by writing appropriate numbers in each hexagon corner to make the given total. Interlocking cubes might be a useful aid.

- Can you tell me what you were doing? Have you any advice for anyone adding large numbers?

Teaching Input 4

- Count on in tens from 100 to 200, and back.
- Now count on in hundreds from 100 to 1000, and back.
- What is $600 − 4$? $300 − 6$? $200 − 10$?
- What is $70 + 64$? And $60 + 40$? And $70 + 26$? And $106 + 4$? And $119 + 9$?
- What is $24 − 20$? What about $66 − 33$? And $99 − 19$? And $99 − 29$? And $99 − 39$? Can you see a pattern?

- How many do I add to 54 to make 84?
- How many do I add to 33 to make 63?
- How many do I add to 99 to make 109?
- What is $301 + 100$? $421 + 100$? $639 + 100$?

Tell the children they are going to use the numbers 3, 5 and 7 and the operators +, − and = to try to make all the numbers from 1 to 50. They may use the numbers in any order, and any one number can be used several times. Both + and − may be used in any sum (for example, $5 + 5 + 7 + 7 = 24$ or $5 + 5 + 7 + 7 − 3 = 21$).

- Have you found all the possibilities? Does anyone have anything different? What did you notice? Is there a pattern or formula you can tell us about?

Teaching Input 5

- If you had to subtract 596 from 604, how would you do it?
- In the same way, how would you work out $636 − 629$? And $742 − 739$?
- What is $95 + 10$? What about $68 + 10$? And 60 plus 30? And $70 + 30$?
- Which three numbers will add up to 50? Are there another three numbers which will add up to 50?
- Add 100 to 37. Now add 100 to 51. And to 11. And to 99.
- If I go into a shop and spend 15p + 50p + 25p + £1, how much do I spend altogether?
- What is 35p + 70p + 50p?
- What is £2 + £1 + £1.50 + 75p?

Repeat several times.

Write the following numbers on the board:

233   150   200   90   42   500

Tell the children they must now use + and −, or a combination of both, to make these numbers. For example, 90 could be made from $30 + 30 + 30$ or $40 + 55 − 5$, and so on.

- Did you work your calculations out in your head or did you use anything to help you?
- Did anyone find a different solution?

Money and Real Life Problems, Making Decisions and Checking Results

This week we are going to continue to develop mathematical strategies and choose appropriate operations. We will also investigate and solve problems involving money and numbers.

OBJECTIVES

- To choose and use appropriate operations (including × and ÷).
- To solve problems involving numbers in real life.
- To use doubling or halving, starting from known facts.

LANGUAGE

double, halve • combinations

RESOURCES

Pupils' Book pages 4 and 5, PCM 3.

Teaching Input 1

- What is half of 12? Of 14? Of 18? Of 28? Of 36? Of 50? Of 100? Of 160? And what is half of 180?

- Can you tell me double 6? Double 7? Double 9? Double 14? Double 18? Double 25? Double 50? Double 80? And double 90?

- What is 2×5? 5×2? 5×4? 4×5? 10×2? 2×10? 5×10? 10×5?

- How would you work out 35×2? Can anyone suggest a different method? *Make sure they suggest 2×35.*

- What is 45×2? How did you work it out? *For example, $(50 \times 2 = 100) - (2 \times 5 = 10) = 90$ or $(2 \times 40 = 80) + (2 \times 5 = 10) = 90$.*

Repeat several times.

- How much would five oranges cost if one costs 10p? How much would ten cost?

- How much would six ice creams cost if one costs 5p?

- Can you tell me some different ways to make 20 using $+$, $-$, $\times$ and $\div$?

Pupils' Book page 4

Ask the children to complete the exercise on Pupils' Book page 4, working out various combinations of money to make given totals and working out any change due.

- What did you buy for £2.50? Did anyone get anything different? Did you check your change?

Teaching Input 2

- If I go into a shop with £3 and I spend £2.75, what change do I get?

- If I go into a shop with £1 and I spend 65p, what change do I get? Did you add on or subtract to work it out?

- I spent 60p and then £1.10. If I had £2.20 to start with, how much have I left?

- What is £1.25 + £1.25 + 50p + 75p?

- What is £1.75 + 25p + £2.50?

- If a spider has eight legs, how many legs are there on two spiders? On five spiders? On ten spiders?

- If 30 people get on a bus and 19 get off, how many are left? If another ten get on, how many are there on the bus now?

- If 3 children share 12 sweets equally among them, how many sweets does each child get?

- If 4 children share out 12 sweets equally, how many will each get?

- There are ten sandwiches and five children. How many sandwiches are there for each child?

Pupils' Book pages 4 and 5

Ask the children to complete the exercise on Pupils' Book page 5 by checking the bills against the prices given on page 4. Remind them that sometimes the item amount is incorrect and sometimes the total bill is incorrect so they must look very carefully.

- Do you think you found all the mistakes? Which ones did you find? Has anyone found any others?

Teaching Input 3

- If I have 50 conkers and I share them equally between five children, how many would each child receive? What about ten children? Or 50 children?

- If I think of a number and I subtract 22, the answer is 46. What was my number?

- I am thinking of a number. I subtract 46 and the answer is 18. What was my number? How did you work it out?

- What is $20 \div 2$? And $20 \div 5$? And $20 \div 10$?

- What is 9×2? 2×9? 5×6? 6×5?

- If it costs £1.10 each to go to the cinema, how much would it cost for two people?

- If a cake costs 50p, how much would two cost? How much would five cost? Four? Ten?

Ask each child to pick three numbers less than 50. Tell them they are going to use the numbers and the operators $+$, $-$, $\times$, $\div$ and $=$ to make exactly 100. They do not need to use all the numbers or operators each time. They can use them as many times as they like. In how many ways can they make 100?

- Did you all manage to make 100 exactly? Could anyone not make 100? How did you get to 100? What numbers did you use?

Teaching Input 4

- If I have £22 and I am given £50, how much do I have altogether?

- I have £100 and I spend £80.50. How much do I have left?

- What silver coins can I use to pay my bill of 75p? What about 60p? Or £1? 90p? 95p?

- How many pennies are there in £2.25? In £10? In £4.65?

- How many pounds are there in 635p and 721p?

- If I have 20 sweets and four children, how many sweets can I give each of them? What if I have ten children? Or five children? Or two?

- If there are six buttons on a card and I need 18, how many cards should I buy? What if I needed 12 buttons? 24 buttons? 30 buttons?

PCM 3

The children complete the table about the Burger Bar on PCM 3.

Teaching Input 5

- What is $50 - 30$? And $50 - 29$? And $50 - 31$? How did you work them out?

- What is $20 + 20$? What is 2×20?

- What is $25 + 25$? What is 2×25? How can you work out 2×25? What about $25 + 25$?

- What is double 12? Double 15? Double 20? Double 25? Double 30? Double 100?

- Which three numbers can be added to make 19? Is there another combination?

- If I go into a burger bar and I buy three packets of chips at 50p each, how much do I pay altogether? What change would I receive from £2?

- I have £2 and I buy a comic for 70p and an ice cream for 50p. How much do I have left?

Ask each child to choose four numbers less than 50, suggesting that two should be quite low, such as 2 or 5. They then decide on a total between 100 and 200 and try to make that number using some or all of their numbers and the operators $+$, $-$, $\times$, $\div$ and $=$.

- Which totals are impossible? Why do you think that is? Are there any you couldn't make?

Measures, including Problems

This week we will be working on measuring using standard units, reading scales and introducing decimal notation for metres. We will also be using units of time and the relationships between them.

- To read scales to the nearest division.
- To measure and compare using standard units.
- To record estimates and measurements to the nearest whole or half unit or in mixed units.
- To suggest suitable units and measuring equipment.
- To use units of time and know the relationship between them.

LANGUAGE

analogue • centimetres, metres, grams, kilograms, litres, millilitres, units of measure, standard units, capacity • metre rule, rulers, tape measures • estimate, check

RESOURCES

Marked litre jugs, containers of different sizes (include those which hold more than a litre and less than a litre), water, rulers, calendar, metre sticks, tape measures, scales, suitable things to weigh (rice, sand, pulses), labels from tins and bottles (collected by the children).

Teaching Input 1

- Playtime lasts for 30 minutes. If it ends at 11.00, what time does it start?
- Abdul walked to school. If he left at 8.45 and arrived at 9.05, how long did he take?
- How many metres are there in a kilometre?
- How many grams are there in a kilogram?
- How many millilitres are there in a litre?
- What would be a suitable standard unit to measure the distance from school to home? To measure the length of the playground? To measure the width of a hand?

litre jugs, containers, water

Adult supervision recommended

Before the children start, draw this table on the board and ask them to copy it. (They do not need to copy the example.)

Item	My estimate (How much?)	Check (How much?)	Correct
1st container	300ml	450ml	No

Now ask the children to estimate and measure the capacity of a beaker and a cup to the nearest 100ml, recording their results on their table.

They should then try to find three bottles or containers which hold less than 1 litre. Ask them to investigate how much they hold to the nearest 100ml.

Teaching Input 2

ruler

- What could we measure in kilograms?
- What could we measure in centimetres? In metres? In millilitres?
- What could we measure in litres? In grams?
- What would be suitable to measure the desk? A book? Round a tree?
- What would we use to measure how much a bottle holds?

Show the children a ruler, blank side outward, and tell them it is 30cm long. Ask the children to estimate where 9.5 centimetres would be and mark it. Check how close they were by turning over the ruler. Repeat this several times for different amounts, each time checking how close the estimate was.

calendar

Showing the calendar, ask questions of different children round the class.

- Can you tell me the date of your birthday? Which day is your birthday on this year?

- Can you write the days of the week in order?

- Can you write down the seasons of the year?

- How many months are there in a year?

- How many minutes are there in one hour? In two hours?

- How many seconds are there in one minute? In four minutes?

- How many days are there in one week? Two weeks? Three? Four?

- How many days are there in one month? Are all months the same?

- How many weeks are there in one month? Is it always the same? Is it ever exactly four weeks?

Teaching Input 3

- Would you expect a door to be two metres or five metres high?

- Would you expect a cup to hold 200 millilitres, 500 millilitres or 1 litre of liquid?

- Would you want to eat 100 grams, 500 grams or 1 kilogram of strawberries?

Ask the children to think of a question to ask the rest of the group on time, length, weight or capacity, for example, 'How long do you think it would take to eat your lunch – 1 minute, 15 minutes or 1 hour?'

rulers, metre sticks, tape measures

Remind the children always to measure objects twice to check, and always to start at the beginning of the measure. Tell them they are going to use a metre stick to measure and record the height of a table, the height of a chair or seat, the height of a friend, and the height of a window sill in metres and centimetres, for example, 1m 5cm.

- Find three things that are longer than 20 centimetres and three things that are shorter. What do they actually measure?

- Now use a ruler to measure the width of the table in centimetres, recording your findings.

- Then measure the length of a pencil and the width of a book. Record your results.

Teaching Input 4

- If one orange weighs 220 grams, how much will four oranges weigh?

- You have 70 litres of water. How many 10 litre containers can you fill? How many containers could you fill with 100 litres of water? With 60 litres?

- You have to fill up ten half-litre bottles. How much water do you need?

- If there are five kilograms of apples in one box, how many kilograms of apples are there in two boxes? In ten boxes? In 100 boxes?

- If it is 4 o'clock now, what time will it be in 45 minutes? In 1 hour 20 minutes? In 3 hours 8 minutes? What time was it 15 minutes ago? What time was it $2\frac{1}{2}$ hours earlier?

scales, suitable things to weigh

Ask the children to work in pairs, recording their findings in their books.

- Find five things that you think weigh more than 100 grams but less than 1 kilogram. Estimate their weights then check them. Record in your books, then write each weight to the nearest 50 or 100 grams.

Then give each pair of children approximately 1 kilogram of rice, sand or pulses. Ask them to estimate and then weigh 100 grams, 200 grams, 250 grams, 500 grams, and then all of it.

- What was the weight of material given to you? Did you find it easy to estimate?

Teaching Input 5

labels from tins and bottles, things to weigh

Ask the children to work in pairs to make the amounts on the labels (for instance, for a 500 gram tin of baked beans, they might weigh out 500 grams of dried beans).

Ask the children to list the days of the week and to write something special about each day. For example, 'On Wednesday I go swimming after school'. Encourage them to say how long they spend on each activity.

Shape and Space

This week we are going to work on 2D and 3D shapes and lines of symmetry, using some practical activities.

OBJECTIVES

- To classify and describe 2D and 3D shapes according to their properties.
- To make and describe shapes and patterns.
- To identify and sketch lines of symmetry and recognise shapes with no lines of symmetry.

LANGUAGE

quadrilateral, square, rectangle, rhombus, kite, trapezium, parallelogram • vertices • parallel, right angles • line of symmetry, symmetrical, reflection

RESOURCES

Selection of 2D and 3D shapes (including squares, rectangles, hexagons, circles and triangles, quadrilaterals, triangular prisms, cones, cylinders, cubes, cuboids), interlocking cubes, PCMs 4, 5 and 6, mirrors, squared paper, coloured pencils.

Teaching Input 1

selection of 2D and 3D shapes

Show the children different 2D shapes and ask them to describe their properties, for example, how many sides each has, whether each side is the same length, and how many corners each has.

- What can you tell me about a square? Is there anything else? *Make sure you discuss the four right angles and that it has four sides of equal length.*
- What can you tell me about a rectangle? Is there anything else?
- What about a rhombus? *Show the children a rhombus and talk about it as 'a square pushed over' with four sides of equal length and in which opposite angles are equal. Point out that the angles added together equal those of a square, that they are four times 90 degrees.*
- Do you know any other quadrilaterals? Do you know a kite? A trapezium? A parallelogram? Can you tell me about their properties?

selection of 2D and 3D shapes, PCM 4, interlocking cubes

Ask the children to complete PCM 4 by looking carefully at the shapes, cutting them out and fitting them into the shape given (it is possible!). Then ask them to use interlocking cubes to make the shapes shown.

- What other models can you make using the shapes without breaking any of them up?

Teaching Input 2

selection of 2D and 3D shapes

- Tell me which shapes are quadrilateral. Make labels for them and put them on display.
- What can you tell me about the square? The rectangle? The rhombus?

Show children lines that are parallel and discuss the meaning of 'parallel lines'. Ask for examples of parallel lines around the classroom.

- What can you tell me about a right angle? *Point out examples in the classroom.*

Now draw their attention to the 3D shapes, pointing to them in turn.

- Can you give me the name of this one? And this one? How many faces has this one got? How many edges? How many vertices, or corners?

Repeat for each shape.

- Can anyone tell me what a hemisphere is? How could we make one?

selection of 2D and 3D shapes, interlocking cubes

Adult supervision recommended

Give each child 24 cubes. Tell them all to make a shape from 12 cubes and to hide it from view. One child describes their shape whilst the other children in the group try to reconstruct the shape from the given description using their remaining cubes. Repeat with the other children's shapes.

- Did you find it easy to describe your shape? Did you find it easy to follow the instructions to build the shapes?

Teaching Input 3

 selection of 2D shapes

Ask the children to use the shapes to make patterns and pictures with a specified set of properties. For example, 'It should have three quadrilaterals, two triangles, and a pentagon'. The children draw around the shapes, colour or cut out and make a pattern or picture. They should be prepared to talk about their creation and discuss the properties of the shapes used.

 interlocking cubes, PCMs 5 and 6

Ask the children to use PCM 5 to complete PCM 6 in which they must fit the oddly-shaped parcels into a lorry. They might like to use interlocking cubes to make the parcels and see if they can fit them into the lorry.

Teaching Input 4

- What do we mean by symmetry?

- How can we check if a shape or pattern has a line of symmetry?

- How can we check if a shape or pattern has two lines of symmetry?

- How can we make a symmetrical picture or pattern?

- Can you tell me the name of the 2D shape that is half a circle?

- Can you tell me the name of a 2D shape that has four equal sides and four right angles?

- Think of a 2D shape and describe it to the group. Can anyone tell me which shape it is?

Repeat until everyone has had a turn describing a shape.

 mirrors, squared paper, coloured pencils

Before the children begin, explain that 'line symmetry' means reflection. Now ask the group to make a 2D picture either by drawing or with cut out shapes. Remind them to sketch in lines of symmetry lightly at first. If necessary, they should check with a mirror. Encourage them to make their picture or pattern detailed and to make the overall picture symmetrical. Ask them to note the shapes which have no lines of symmetry.

Reasoning about Shapes

This week we will be working on solving mathematical puzzles, investigating and explaining methods and reasoning.

OBJECTIVES

- To solve mathematical problems or puzzles, explain methods and discuss reasoning.
- To recognise simple patterns and relationships.

LANGUAGE

symmetry, line of symmetry

RESOURCES

Triangular dotted paper, coloured pens, Pupils' Book page 6, 5 × 5 pinboard, pins, 2D shapes, squared paper, PCM 7, dice (1 to 6) or (1 to 9).

Teaching Input 1

- Can you tell me a rule for odd numbers? For even numbers? Do they always work?
- Tell me two odd numbers between 70 and 80.
- Can you think of three odd numbers between 90 and 100?
- How could you make an even number into an odd number?
- How can you make an odd number into an even one?
- What happens when you add two odd numbers?
- What happens when you add two even numbers?
- What happens when you add one odd number and one even number?
- What happens when you add two odd numbers and one even number?
- What happens when you add two even numbers and one odd number?
- Give me some examples to prove these statements. Can we say these are rules?

triangular dotted paper, coloured pens
Give the children a sheet of triangular dotted paper each and coloured pens in three colours. Ask them to draw triangles of different sizes with triangles within triangles.

Encourage them to colour each triangle a different colour and to investigate how many triangles can be found within each large one.

Teaching Input 2

- What is 25 + 15? Explain how you worked it out.
- What is 18 + 13? How did you find the answer?
- What is 25 × 2? How did you calculate it?
- What is 40 ÷ 2? How did you work it out?
- What is 50 ÷ 2? How did you find the answer?
- What is 4 × 5? And 5 × 4? And 4 × 10? 10 × 4? 5 × 6? 6 × 5?
- What can you tell me about multiplying numbers?
- Can you give me a multiplication sum? What happens when you reverse the numbers?
- How can I recognise that a shape is a square?
- How can I recognise that a shape is a rectangle?
- Is there a rule?
- Where can I see a right angle? How do I know that is a right angle?

Pupils' Book page 6, 5 × 5 pinboard, pins

Give the children Pupils' Book page 6 and have ready a pinboard and pins. Ask them to investigate the number of squares or rectangles they can make on a 3 × 3 pinboard. (Go over the 3 × 3 work before telling them to progress to 4 × 4 and 5 × 5 pinboards.)

- Did everyone get the same answers? Did anyone find anything different? How many squares did you get? *It is possible to get 6.*
- Do you think there would be a pattern? What if you had a 4 × 4 pinboard?
- What if you had a 5 × 5 pinboard – how many squares would you get?

Teaching Input 3

 2D shapes, squared paper

Give the children the shapes and ask them to combine two, three or four of them on squared paper to make a symmetrical pattern or picture. They should draw round the

shapes to record the pattern. Repeat this two or three times with different patterns, then ask the group to point out the lines of symmetry.

Teaching Input 4

 PCM 7, dice (1 to 6 or 1 to 9)

The children play this game with a partner, using PCM 7 as a scorecard. They will need a 1 to 6 or 1 to 9 dice, as appropriate. Each pair decides whether to use highest or lowest numbers as their target, before taking it in turns to throw the dice and decide which box to put the score in. They can use a box in their own column, or put it in one of the other player's boxes. After three turns each, the one with the highest or lowest number (as decided) wins five points. After five or ten games, the one with the highest score wins.

- Did you use any strategies when playing the game? What were they? Does anyone else have any others?

Counting and Properties of Number, Reasoning about Numbers

This week we are going to be doing number work on multiples of 2, 5 and 10, and solving problems.

OBJECTIVES

- To solve mathematical problems and explain methods.
- To recognise familiar multiples.
- To investigate general statements about familiar numbers.
- To describe and extend number sequences.
- To count on or back in a variety of ways.

LANGUAGE

multiples, digits • pattern, diagonals

RESOURCES

Pupils' Book pages 7, 8 and 9, PCM 8, squared paper.

Teaching Input 1

- Count on in tens, from 110 to 200 and back.
- Count on in tens, from 97 to 197 and back.
- What can you tell me about these two counts? Is there a rule for counting in tens? What is it?
- What is the rule if you count in twos, starting at zero?
- Tell me the even numbers between 76 and 90.
- Tell me the odd numbers between 71 and 89.
- Now count on in threes from 0 to 30.
- This time count on in fours from 0 to 32.
- Try counting backwards from 30 in threes and from 32 in fours.
- What are the multiples of 2?
- What are the multiples of 10?
- What are the multiples of 5? What can you tell me about multiples of 5?

Pupils' Book page 7

Give the children Pupils' Book page 7. Ask them to work through the questions using the number and operator 'buttons' as many times as they like to make each screen number. How many ways can they make each target?

Teaching Input 2

- What are the multiples of 10 up to 200?
- Count on in fifties from 0 to 500, and back.
- Can you tell me all the multiples of 5 to 95?
- Is 63 a multiple of 10, 5 or 2?
- Is 40 a multiple of 10, 5 or 2?
- Add 46 + 9. What is 36 + 11? How did you work them out?
- What is double 11? Double 12? Double 13? Double 14? Double 15? Double 18? Double 25?
- What is half of 100? Of 50? Of 30? Of 40? Of 36?
- Continue the pattern 115, 120, 125 … to 200.
- What is the sequence 115, 118, 121? Can you continue it?

Pupils' Book page 8

Ask the children to complete the missing numbers in the schemes on Pupils' Book page 8.

- Can you explain what you have been doing? What can you tell me about the diagonal? What happens when you follow it? *Remind them to look at the difference between the numbers on the diagonals.*

Teaching Input 3

- What is $50 - 31$? $50 - 29$? $73 - 19$? $73 - 21$? How did you work them out?

- What happens if you add numbers in a different order? Give me an example.

- What is 5×6 and 6×5? What about 10×2 and 2×10? Can you explain the results? Is there a rule?

- Work out $10 \div 2$, $20 \div 2$, $20 \div 10$, $50 \div 10$.

- Now tell me how many tens there are in 50, 100 and 500.

Tell the children they can use $+$, $-$, $\times$ and $\div$ to make some numbers.

- How many ways can you make 19? For example, $100 - 81 = 19$.

- How did you make 19? Did anyone do it differently?

- Did you check any of your answers? How? Which was the hardest part?

Teaching Input 4

- Give me three numbers which add up to 22, to 40, to 75, to 100 and 125.

- Tell me two numbers which add up to 75, to 84 and to 96.

- Can you give me two numbers which will add up to 34, to 62, to 19 and to 55?

- There are three numbers less than 10 that can be shared equally into three parts. Which numbers are they?

- I am thinking of a number and it has three digits. What could it be? *Do not start with a specific number to begin. As the ideas come in, introduce limits, such as 'it is odd'. Play the game several times.*

PCM 8, squared paper

Give the children PCM 8 and some squared paper, and ask them to play the 'Snake Game'. They should use the paper to design their snakes, forming them from three or four squares. The key is to make snakes of different shapes and patterns. They then cover numbers on the 199-square to try to make the largest or smallest number they can (by totalling all the squares covered by their snake). This can also be extended to trying to get as close as possible to given target numbers.

Teaching Input 5

Play again the 'I am thinking of a 3-digit number' game from yesterday.

- How many questions does it take to find the number? Let us try again with another 3-digit number.

- Can you tell me how many hundreds, tens and units are there in 151, in 364 and in 721?

Pupils' Book page 9

Ask the children to play 'Find Forty' using Pupils' Book page 9. Hidden in the grid are seven 2×2 squares which add up to 40. Can the group find all the sets?

Understanding × and ÷, and Mental Calculation Strategies

- To know by heart multiplication facts for the 2, 5 and 10 times-tables.
- To understand multiplication as repeated addition and that it can be done in any order.
- To understand division as grouping.
- To use known facts to carry out mentally simple multiplication or division.

LANGUAGE

digits • multiplication, square

RESOURCES

PCM 9, calculators, dice, paper, pencils.

This week we are going to work on × and ÷ and use known facts to carry out simple multiplication and division.

Teaching Input 1

- What is 2 × 4 and 4 × 2? What about 4 ÷ 2?
- Tell me double 10, double 12, double 14, double 16, double 18 and double 20.
- What is double 11? Double 13? Double 15? Double 17? Double 19?
- What are the multiples of 10 between 0 and 100? And of 5?
- What are the multiples of 2 from 0 to 40?
- If six books are shared equally between two children, how many will each get? How many will three children receive?
- If 12 books are shared equally between two children, how many will each get? How many will three children receive?
- What is 12 ÷ 1? Or 14 ÷ 1?
- How many fives are there in 15? 25? 40?

Ask the children to play 'Make 100' in their books. They choose four numbers between 1 and 9 (which can be used more than once) and one number between 10 and 100 (which can be used once only). They also use the operators ×, ÷, + and − (used once only). The aim is that they make 100 using their chosen numbers. For example, if they picked 4, 6, 7, 9 and 50, they might do 9 × 6 = 54;

50 + 54 = 104; 104 − 4 = 100. How many different ways can they do this?

Pick new numbers and repeat the activity.

Teaching Input 2

- What is half of 300? Of 400? Of 600?
- What is double 5? Double 50? Double 500?
- What is 7 × 5? So what is 35 ÷ 5?
- What is 5 × 7? So what is 35 ÷ 7?
- Can you share 20 between 10? Between 5? Between 2?
- What happens when you multiply 7 × 10, 7 × 100, 6 × 10 and 6 × 100?
- Can you share 21 between 3?
- Multiply 5 × 2, 6 × 2, 7 × 2 and 10 × 2.

PCM 9

Give the children PCM 9 and draw the following on the board.

6	7	8
12	14	16
18	21	24

(Tell them to ignore the instructions on the PCM which refer to tomorrow's work.)

- Ask them to find these numbers on their PCM.
- Add all the shaded numbers and record your total.
- Add all the corner numbers and record your total.
- Multiply the centre number by 4. What do you find?
- What do you think will happen if you pick another 3 × 3 square on your PCM?

- What have you discovered? Is there a rule or a pattern? Can you describe it?

Teaching Input 3

- You have eggboxes with six spaces, and you have 24 eggs. How many boxes do you need? And for 30 eggs?
- If there are ten children and 50 cakes, how many cakes will each child get? What if there are 30 cakes? Or 20 cakes?
- My bus ticket costs 50p. How much would five tickets cost? Three tickets? Ten?
- Share 14 sweets equally between four children. How many sweets are left over?
- What is half of 28? How did you work it out? What is a quarter of 28?
- What is half of 100? And quarter of 100?
- What are 5 × 4, 4 × 5, 20 ÷ 5 and 20 ÷ 4?

PCM 9, calculators

Provide the children with PCM 9 and ask them to work through the instructions. Note that this may need to be introduced to the children and if they work with high numbers they may need a calculator.

- Can you explain your work? Look for patterns – do they always work? Was it necessary to use a calculator?

Teaching Input 4

- Tell me the multiples of 2, 5 and 10. Are there any rules about them?
- How many hundreds, tens and units are there in 524? 631? 501? 111?

- What is 10 × 2? 2 × 10? 15 × 2? 25 × 2?
- What is half of 20, 40 and 80? What is a quarter of 4, 8, 12? How do you know that?
- How much do I pay for two tickets costing 50p each? For two tickets costing £5 each? For two tickets costing £50 each?
- I have 50 pencils. If one pencil case holds ten pencils, how many cases do I need?

dice, paper, pencils

Ask the children to play the 'Number Game' in groups of up to four players. Each group will need two dice, some paper and a pencil. Each player takes turns to throw the two dice and multiply the numbers together. That is their first score. They continue playing, adding their multiplied scores cumulatively as they proceed, until one reaches 200 and wins.

This game can be varied by using more than two dice, adding the first two numbers and multiplying that by the third. You might also try having a larger target total or starting the children at 500 and subtracting the scores to reach zero to win.

Teaching Input 5

- If I have 12 children and four tables, how many chairs do I need for each table? Is there another way to seat the children?
- If I want an equal number on each table, how many will sit on each? Can I have an even number on each table?

Provide the children with sets of three numbers between 1 and 10 and ask them to find the multiplication totals. For example, you might give them 6, 3 and 4.
6 × 3 × 4 = 72.

- What can you tell me about your work? Did you check it? How? Has anyone any questions or observations? Did you all get the same total in a different way?

Money and Real Life Problems, Making Decisions and Checking Results

This week we are going to solve problems and explain our working.

OBJECTIVES

- To solve problems involving numbers and money.
- To explain methods orally and writing.
- To understand and use £.p notation.

LANGUAGE

combination, possibilities, statements, symbols

RESOURCES

PCM 10, Pupil's Book pages 10 and 11.

Teaching Input 1

- Can you tell me how many pence there are in £1, £2.75, £5 and £4.64?
- How many 10p coins make £1? And £10?
- How many 20p coins make £1?
- How many 50p coins make £1? And £5?
- If Mary has two 20p pieces, a 50p and a 10p coin, how much has she altogether?
- I go into a shop with £2 and spend £1.75. How much have I left?
- If three chocolate bars cost 27p each and I have £1, how much change will I get?
- I am thinking of a number. If I double it and add 10, the answer is 32. What was my number?

Pupils' Book page 10
Ask the children to complete the Pupils' Book exercise, working out combinations of prices in a bookshop.

- Which books did you buy? In what combinations? Did you always have money left? Was it possible to buy books and spend exactly £10?

Teaching Input 2

- I have 22 apples, 14 oranges and 24 pears. How many pieces of fruit have I altogether?

How did you work it out? If I put the fruit into ten boxes, how many pieces of fruit will be in each box? If I have five boxes, how many pieces will be in each box?

Repeat several times.

- I am thinking of a number. If I halve it and add 5, the answer is 30. What was my number?
- Each bear has four paws. How many paws do five bears, six bears and ten bears have?

Repeat several times.

- I go into a post office and buy 12 stamps. Each one costs 5p. How much do I pay?

 Play 'Back to one'. Ask the children to start at any number up to and including 500. They should divide even numbers by 2; if the resultant number is odd, add 1 and divide the result by 2, and so on. For example, if the number was 60: $60 \div 2 = 30 \div 2 = 15 + 1 = 16 \div 2 = 8 \div 2 = 4 \div 2 = 2 \div 2 = 1$.

How long can the children make their chains?

- Who has the longest chain? How did you make it? Have you found all the possibilities? What could you do next?

Teaching Input 3

- If an ice cream costs 63p and a drink costs 90p, how much are they altogether?

- Drinks cost 90p each. How much will two cost?

- What is 160 − 60? 174 − 24? 135 + 55? 14 × 2? 20 × 2? 50 × 2? How did you work it out?

- An octopus has eight legs. How many legs do two, five and ten octopuses have?

- How many pence are there in £5 and £4.63?

- How many pounds are there in 632p and 710p?

Pupils' Book page 11

Ask the children to do the 'Circle Investigation' in the Pupils' Book. They may use the symbols +, −, ×, ÷ and =, and the numbers in the circles to make statements.

- What totals can you make?

- Can you make some numbers in different ways?

Teaching Input 4

- How many ways can we make £1 using silver coins?

- There are ten buttons on a card. How many are there on two, three, five, ten and twenty cards?

Write on the board some amounts of money, such as 50p, 100p, £3, £2.50 and 262p. Ask the children to work out combinations of four smaller amounts which will make the totals given, recording their solutions as additions.

- What have you been doing? How many different ways did you find to make the same amount? Has anyone a different combination?

Teaching Input 5

- I think of a number, double it and add 15. My answer is 45, so what was my number?

- I think of a number, double it and add 20. My answer is 60, so what was my number?

- What is 300 + 426? 521 + 320? 631 + 250? How did you work them out?

Repeat several times.

- What is 50 ÷ 2? 50 ÷ 5? 50 ÷ 10? 9 ÷ 3? 12 ÷ 3? 15 ÷ 3?

Repeat several times.

- There are 25 beanbags. If John takes 7 and Ravi takes 12, how many are there left?

Repeat several times.

PCM 10

Ask the children to complete the 'Bees in the hive' by finding ways of making the amounts at the top of each hive. The last two hives are left blank for them to put in their own amounts.

- Can you explain your work? Are some amounts more difficult to create than others?

Fractions

This week we are going to work on fractions in a variety of contexts, using and understanding the associated language.

OBJECTIVES

- To recognise unit fractions and use them to find fractions of shapes and numbers.
- To begin to recognise simple fractions that are several parts of a whole.
- To begin to recognise simple equivalent fractions.

LANGUAGE

part, fraction • one whole, one half, one quarter, one third, one tenth.

RESOURCES

4 × 4 square (with two shaded squares and two not shaded), 6 × 2 rectangle divided into six with three shaded sections, 5 × 2 rectangle (divided into ten sections with five shaded), interlocking cubes (two colours), PCMs 11 and 12, number line graded in halves, Pupils' Book pages 12 and 13.

Teaching Input 1

4 × 4 square, 6 × 2 rectangle, 5 × 2 rectangle

- What is half of 10? Of 12? Of 14? Of 20? What is quarter of 4? Of 12? Of 20?
- Tell me one tenth of 10. Of 20. Of 30.
- Now count on in fives from 0 to 20.
- How many fives are in 20?
- What would one quarter of 20 be?
- Can anyone tell me the fractions they know?
- Can you show me another way of writing $\frac{2}{4}$? Show the 4 by 4 square and explain that this is $\frac{2}{4}$ which is the same as $\frac{1}{2}$ or a half. *Use the board to demonstrate writing fractions.*
- What about $\frac{3}{6}$? Show the 6 × 2 rectangle and explain that this is $\frac{3}{6}$ which is also the same as $\frac{1}{2}$ or a half.
- What about $\frac{5}{10}$? Show the 5 × 2 rectangle and tell the children that this is $\frac{5}{10}$, which is also the same as $\frac{1}{2}$ or a half.

interlocking cubes
Adult supervision recommended

Play 'Models of Fractions' using two colours of interlocking cubes. Ask the children to make a shape or model to show one quarter, for example, a rectangle with one red and three blue sections, or a 4 × 4 square.

- Can you make different shapes to show $\frac{1}{2}$ and $\frac{3}{4}$?

Make labels to put with the models, then repeat the activity using 10 cubes.

- Can you make shapes to show $\frac{1}{10}$? For instance, 1 red and 9 blue cubes.

Continue until they have shown you the full range from $\frac{1}{10}$ to 1 whole.

Finally, as a group, make a display illustrating different ways of showing $\frac{1}{4}, \frac{1}{2}, \frac{3}{4}$ and different ways of showing $\frac{1}{10}, \frac{2}{10}$... up to 1 whole.

- Look at the shapes you have made. What can you tell me about your work? Look at the models showing $\frac{5}{10}$. What do you notice about them? Is there another way of expressing $\frac{5}{10}$? What about $\frac{2}{4}$? Can you think of another fraction which could be expressed in this way? What about $\frac{4}{8}$?

Teaching Input 2

number line

Show the children the number line graded in halves and ask them questions.

- If I have $\frac{1}{2}$ and another $\frac{1}{2}$, how much do I have?

- If I have 2 and another $\frac{1}{2}$, how much do I have?
- Which number is halfway between 4 and 3?
- Which number is halfway between 2 and 3?
- Which number is halfway between 1 and 2?
- Who can tell me how many quarters there are in a half, in three quarters and in one whole?
- Which is larger, $\frac{1}{2}$ or $\frac{1}{4}$? What about $\frac{1}{2}$ or $\frac{3}{4}$?
- Which is larger, $\frac{5}{10}$ or $\frac{1}{2}$?
- Which is larger, $\frac{4}{8}$ or $\frac{1}{2}$?
- If my book has 100 pages, where would halfway be?

It is helpful to point out that half of $\frac{1}{2}$ is $\frac{1}{4}$.

PCM 11

Ask the children to complete the fractions on the PCM.

- What can you tell me about your work? What have you discovered?
- What is $\frac{3}{4}$ of 8? What is $\frac{1}{4}$ of 8?

Repeat the questions for other fractions on the sheet.

Teaching Input 3

- How many quarters make $\frac{1}{2}$?
- How many quarters are there in one whole?
- How many halves are there in one whole?
- If I have $\frac{3}{4}$ and I add another $\frac{1}{4}$, how much do I have? *If necessary, show a 4 × 4 square with three squares shaded as a great deal of practical experience is needed by the children at this early stage.*
- How else could I write $\frac{5}{10}$? What about $\frac{3}{6}$, $\frac{4}{8}$, and $\frac{2}{4}$?

Pupils' Book page 12

Ask the children to write the fractions shown in the Pupils' Book.

- What have you noticed about the fractions? Did you find any awkward to work out? Which did you find easiest?

Teaching Input 4

- Which is the greater, $\frac{1}{4}$ or $\frac{1}{2}$? $\frac{3}{4}$ or $\frac{1}{2}$? $\frac{5}{10}$ or $\frac{1}{2}$? $\frac{4}{8}$ or $\frac{1}{2}$? $\frac{2}{8}$ or $\frac{1}{4}$?
- If I add $\frac{1}{3}$ and $\frac{2}{3}$, what do I have altogether?
- What is $\frac{3}{4}$ add $\frac{1}{4}$?
- What comes halfway between 5 and 10?
- What comes halfway between 7 and 8?
- What comes halfway between 9 and 10?
- Can you explain what $\frac{1}{3}$ is? *They may need to draw a rectangle made up of three squares with one shaded.*

Draw lots of different-shaped rectangles on the board with different fractions coloured in. Ask individual children to come to the front and write what fraction is shown by each shaded area.

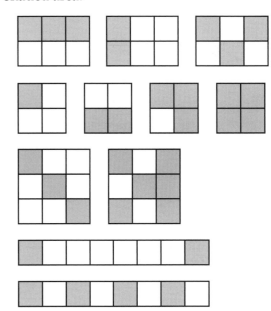

- Were the fractions easy to work out? How did you do them? Did you have to count the squares each time or could you recognise some of them?

Teaching Input 5

PCM 12, Pupils' Book page 13

Ask the children to complete the PCM and the work on Pupils' Book page 13 to consolidate their work and to give you an indication of their understanding.

Understanding +, −, Time including Problems, Making Decisions and Checking Results

This week we are working on investigations, patterns and understanding of addition and subtraction and solving problems.

OBJECTIVES

- To use knowledge that addition can be done in any order to do mental calculations more efficiently.
- To use known number facts to add and subtract mentally.
- To read and begin to write the vocabulary related to time.

LANGUAGE

horizontal, vertical, diagonal • digital, analogue

RESOURCES

PCM 13, analogue and digital clocks, timers (1-minute and 10-minute) square dotted paper.

Teaching Input 1

- Add together 115 + 225 + 35. How did you work it out?
- Add 95 + 63. How did you calculate it?
- What is 230 − 30 and 650 − 230? How do you know?
- Which three numbers will make 50 when added together? What about 90 or 150?
- How many do you add to 40 to make 100? 150? 67?
- What is the total of 12 + 15? Of 12 + 17 + 10?
- How many more than 5 are 49 and 50?

Repeat each question format several times.

- Can each of you, in turn, ask the group a sum using + and −?

 Adult supervision recommended

Draw the following diagram on the board:

- Add each pair of neighbouring numbers. (2 + 3 = 5, 3 + 4 = 7, 4 + 5 = 9, 5 + 6 = 11, 6 + 2 = 8.)

- Now add all these totals together. What do you get?
- Change the position of some numbers to try and make higher and lower totals. What do you discover?
Change the arrangement but keep the same numbers.

- What have you found out? Can you explain your work?
- Could you make or find a rule?

Teaching Input 2

- Add 16 + 12 + 5 + 4.
- Add 18 + 10 + 12.
- What about 18 + 12 + 10?
- How many hundreds, tens and units are there in 216? 314? 462? 814? 330 and 951?

Repeat several times.

- What do you do when you add 63 + 29? 14 + 23? 140 + 800?
- What is 192 + 6? 752 + 2? 769 + 5? 80 + 25? 60 + 76? 45 + 23?

Repeat several times.

- What do you add to 992 to reach 1000? To get from 998 to 1000? To get from 1000 to 1009?

Repeat several times.

PCM 13

Ask the children to complete the PCM by following the instructions above each arrow.

 • Can you describe what you have been doing? Can you see a pattern?

Teaching Input 3

 analogue and digital clocks

• How many seconds are there in a minute?

• How many minutes are there in an hour?

• How many hours are there in a day?

Show the children the analogue clock and ask them to read the time – quarter past, half past, quarter to, 6 o'clock, 9 o'clock and 12 o'clock. Then ask them to read 5 past 6, ten past 6, quarter past 6, twenty minutes past 6 and half past 6.

Now look at a digital clock, asking the children to read 6:05, 6:20 and 6:15.

Compare analogue and digital times and repeat the exercise with other times.

 1-minute and 10-minute timers

Draw the following table on the board and ask the children to copy it into their books.

What I can do in 1 minute	What I can do in 10 minutes	What I can do in 1 hour

Encourage them to find things to do and check if their estimates were correct by using a 1-minute and 10-minute timer.

 • Discuss what you can do in 1 minute. Did anyone do anything different? Did the time pass quickly? Were any of your guesses wildly wrong?

Teaching Input 4

 • How long does it take to drink a glass of water?

• How long does it take to watch a film?

• How long does it take to eat lunch?

• How long do you think playtime is?

• How long are you at school?

• How long do you sleep at night?

 square dotted paper

Draw the following on the board before playing 'Squares' in pairs.

```
•   •   •   •   •   •
  10  7   9   15  12
•   •   •   •   •   •
  5   3   8   15  10
•   •   •   •   •   •
  22  14  6   30  11
•   •   •   •   •   •
  9   20  10  18  5
•   •   •   •   •   •
  14  17  14  21  17
•   •   •   •   •   •
```

Ask the children, in their pairs, to copy the diagram on square dotted paper.

Players take it in turns to draw a line, either vertical or horizontal, joining two adjacent dots. The player who completes a box scores the number in that box and also has a second turn. When there are no more spare lines, the scores are all added up; the highest score wins.

 • What numbers did you get? What totals?

• Did anyone get a higher total? What numbers did you have?

• What was the smallest total? Which numbers did you have?

• Did anyone get a different total? Which numbers added up to that total?

Teaching Input 5

 • What is double 5? Double 6? Double 7? Double 8? Double 9? Double 10? Double 20?

• What is double 50? Double 25? Double 100? Double 200 and 250?

• What is half of 16? Of 18? 20, 12 and 14?

• What is 2×5? 5×2? 2×6? 6×2? 10×2? 10×5?

 Ask the children to choose any five numbers in the range 1 to 9.

• How many different sums can you make with these numbers using the operations $+, -, \times, \div$ and $=$? Try making all the totals to 50.

 • How many different totals did you make? What is the highest and the lowest total? Have you made the same total using different methods? Have you made all the totals up to 50? Which could you not make?

Handling Data

This week we will be concentrating on Venn and Carroll diagrams and using these diagrams to sort numbers and shapes according to their properties.

OBJECTIVES

- To use Venn and Carroll diagrams to organise and interpret data.

LANGUAGE

diagram, Venn diagram, Carroll diagram • regions, areas, intersection • sort, set

RESOURCES

Selection of 2D shapes (in different colours and sizes), large sheets of paper, paper or card, pencils, number cards (1 to 30), Pupils' Book page 14.

Teaching Input 1

 selection of 2D shapes, large sheets of paper

Draw a simple Venn diagram as below. It is necessary to draw the rectangle in order to contain everything <u>not</u> in the Venn circle.

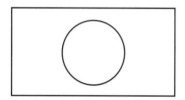

Tell the children that what has been chosen must go in the circle and everything else goes outside it in the rectangle.

Have a selection of 2D triangles available in three colours and start by putting the red ones inside the circle and the others outside it. Ask the children to explain what you are doing and make labels to put in the areas, for example 'Red' and 'Not red'.

 large sheets of paper, pencils, 2D shapes

Adult supervision recommended

The children should work in pairs. They should use the large sheets of paper to draw the diagrams on. Draw the following diagram on the board for them to copy.

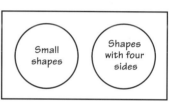

Ask the children to sort shapes into the sets 'small shapes' and 'shapes with four sides'. Discuss whether the small squares should be in with the small shapes, or in the circle with the shapes with four sides, or where?

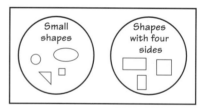

When they have completed the first Venn diagram, repeat the activity with a Venn intersection diagram.

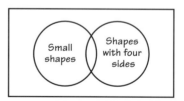

- What do you put into the intersection?
- Why do you put that there?
- Should anything be outside the circle?
- Have you put all the correct shapes in the intersection?

Teaching Input 2

selection of 2D shapes

Continue sorting sets into intersection Venn diagrams using the different-coloured shapes.

Ask the children to label a new intersection Venn diagram with 'red' and 'circles' or 'blue' and 'squares' or 'yellow' and 'triangles'.

Discuss why you put shapes in certain sections.

- Should any be outside in the rectangle?
- Can you tell me about your intersections?

Now ask the children to produce their own criteria for the diagrams. They must be able to explain and make labels for the areas.

number cards (1 to 30), large sheets of paper

The children should work in pairs, each with a set of number cards. Shuffle the pack and place face down.

Write in the circles of a new Venn diagram: 'even numbers' and 'numbers greater than 20'.

1. Ask the children to select two cards and place the numbers in the correct circle. Repeat five times.
2. Ask what the children did with the numbers that did not go into the circles.

Start again.

1. Put odd numbers in one circle and numbers greater than 20 in the other, this time with an intersection in the diagram.

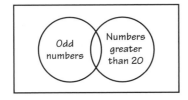

- Now put the numbers in the correct area
- Have you put all the numbers in the correct area?
- What do you discover?
- What about the intersection?
- What about outside the circles?
- Can you ask a question about your diagram?
- Could you develop this work?

Teaching Input 3

selection of 2D shapes, large sheets of paper

Draw a Carroll diagram on a sheet of paper.

Red	Not red

Ask the children to sort the shapes into the two sets 'red' and 'not red'

Draw another diagram.

	Red	Not red
Triangles		
Not triangles		

Discuss the diagram and work as a group to complete the exercise.

- Why do we put this here?
- Is this in the right space?
- Can you ask questions about this?

selection of 2D shapes, paper or card, pencils

Children should work in pairs, drawing a large Carroll diagram on their paper. They may need help to make it large enough. They should be ready with card for labels and a selection of shapes. They then sort the shapes according to the criteria.

	Blue	Not blue
Squares		
Not squares		

Note: To make group work easier, the criteria can be altered, perhaps 'large rectangles', 'not large rectangles', and so on.

Pupils' Book page 14

Ask the children to work through this page, sorting more numbers into Carroll diagrams.

- Can you tell me about your work? Is it easy to look at the information on a Carroll diagram? What about a Venn diagram – is it easy to look at the information in it? Which do you prefer? Why?

Place Value, Ordering, Estimating and Rounding

This week we will read and write numbers to 1000, compare numbers and give a number which lies between them.

OBJECTIVES

- To know what each digit represents and partition numbers.
- To compare two given 3-digit numbers, say which is more or less, and give a number which lies between them.

LANGUAGE

hundreds, tens, units • words, figures • halfway • larger, greater, fewer, less

RESOURCES

Number cards (1 to 9), PCM 9, PCM 14, squared paper, Pupils' Book page 15, reading books.

Teaching Input 1

- How many hundreds, tens and units are there in 634? In 725? In 958? In 1011?

- Which number is equivalent to 3 hundreds, 2 tens and 9 units?

- Which number is equivalent to 5 hundreds, 3 tens and 6 units?

Repeat several times.

- If I want to go from 323 to 523, how might I get there? Could I just add 200?

- How do I change 605 to 655?

- How do I change 824 to 1024?

- Which is greater, 216 or 621?

- Which number is halfway between 40 and 50?

- Which number is halfway between 4 and 5?

- Which number is halfway between 5 and 15?

Repeat several times.

number cards (1 to 9)

You will need three sets of number cards.

Shuffle the sets together. Ask each child to take three cards and to make the largest number they can with them.

The first child then places their cards face up on a table and says the number they have made. The second child takes three more cards and makes the nearest possible number to the first child's before placing it above the first number (if it is higher) or below it (if it is lower), as appropriate. Continue until all the children have put their cards in order. Then encourage the group to check that the numbers are in numerical order, and to rearrange them if they are not. When all the cards have been ordered, ask the children to tell you what each digit represents, for example, 931 is 'nine hundred and thirty-one' or 'nine hundreds, three tens and one unit'.

Repeat the activity, this time making the smallest number possible.

Teaching Input 2

PCM 9, PCM 14, squared paper

Using PCM 9 (a 100-square) or PCM 14 (a 101–200 square), ask the children to play the 'Snake Game', previously played in Unit 7, for 5 minutes. As before, they should use the paper to design their snakes, forming them from three or four squares. They then cover numbers on the PCM to try to make the largest or smallest number they can (by totalling all the squares covered by their snake).

Pupils' Book page 15

Ask the children to complete the 'Matching numbers' activity in the Pupils' Book in which they convert words in numbers to words in numerals and vice-versa.

- Which numbers were most difficult? How did you write those numbers? Which way is easier? Do you all agree?

Teaching Input 3

reading books

- If I have 323 and add 100, what do I get?
- If I have 276 and add 100, what is my new number?

Repeat several times.

- Which is more, £1.50 or £1.15?
- Write on a piece of paper £3.65, 97p, £2.50, £1.50, £6.45 and £5.30. Now write them in order, smallest first.
- If my book has 400 pages, where would halfway be?

- Look at a reading book but do not open it yet. How many pages do you think it has? Why? Does anyone think differently? How do you think the pages halfway will be numbered? Now open it at about halfway. How close were you?
- If a book has 300 pages, where do you think halfway would be?
- Now round these numbers to the nearest 100: 423, 433, 450, 660, 650, 856.

number cards (1 to 9)

Give each child a set of number cards and ask them to shuffle them. The children then pick three cards at random and make all the possible 3-digit numbers, recording in their books. They should then write the numbers in order, smallest to largest, and repeat until they have made five sets. Now ask them to order all the numbers they have made, largest first.

- Tell me some of your 3-digit numbers. How many hundreds, tens and units do they have? Which is your smallest number? Which is your largest?

Understanding + and −, Mental Calculation Strategies

This week we are going to work on addition and subtraction, and develop mental strategies. We will also revise the use of symbols.

Teaching Input 1

- Can you answer quickly 96 + 10? 62 + 100? 28 + 9? 29 + 11? And 27 + 9?
- Which two numbers add up to 21? Are there any others? Can anyone suggest any more? Now tell me two numbers which add up to 34. And to 27. Are there any more for each of those?
- What do I add to 9 to make 21?
- What do I add to 11 to make 20? To make 30?
- What coins could you use to pay £2 and £2.50?

Repeat the questions for several examples.

Draw a simple spider's web on the board and ask the children to copy it in their books. Now, to demonstrate the exercise, write a number in the centre and two sums which make that number caught in the web's strands.

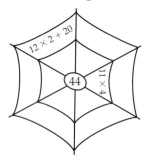

Ask the children to think of a 2-digit total, and write it in the centre of their own web.

They should then use the operations +, −, × and ÷ to make that centre number. They should try to fill all the web segments with different sums. If they find it difficult to draw the web, they can simply list the twelve sums.

- Can you explain what you have been doing? What different sums have you made?
- Did you use +, −, × and ÷ each time? What combinations did you use? Did you manage a different sum in every segment?

Teaching Input 2

- Can you tell me the difference between 41 and 30? 43 and 21? 69 and 40? 73 and 21?

Repeat several times.

- If I take a number away from 60 and the answer is 20, what is the number?
- If 33 is taken away from a number leaving 14, what is the number?
- What is 36p − 21p? 45p − 20p? 50p − 25p?
- What is double 12? Double 13? Double 20?

Ask the children to write down their phone number, or write the school phone number on the board, for example, 615239. Tell them they may use any or all of these numbers and the + and − operators to make all the numbers up to 50 (or 100, if more appropriate). Remind them to write down all their workings in their books.

- Are there any numbers you cannot make? If not, why not?

- Can you make some numbers in several ways?

- Were there any numbers you could not make? Why not? Which numbers were made in several ways?

- Did you spot any patterns?

Teaching Input 3

- Add 55 + 13. How did you work it out?

- What about 63 + 14? And 76 + 12?

- Can you add 55 + 32? How did you find the answer?

Repeat several times.

- What is 508 − 499? How did you work it out?

- What is 36 + 36?

- What is 34 + 34?

- Continue this pattern: $2 + 5 = 7$
$$20 + 50 = 70$$

- Now try another one: $9 + 3 = 12$
$$90 + 30 = 120$$

number cards (0 to 10), paper, pencils

Ask the children, in pairs, to play the game '1 to 25'. Each pair must shuffle and place their cards face down, and choose four cards each. Using their four cards, they should try and make every number from 1 to 25. They may use any number *only once* in an operation but they may use + and − as often as they like. Each child scores 1 point every time they use one of their numbers. For example, if a player has picked the cards 3, 6, 8, and 9 and has to make 14, she might write $3 + 8 + 9 − 6$, scoring 4 points. The winner is the one with the highest score.

- How did you get on with the game? Did you manage to make every number?

- How did you make 42? How did you make 3? Did anyone work them out differently?

Teaching Input 4

- We are going to use 5, 10 and 15 to write down some number sentences. For example, $5 + 10 = 15$ is 5 plus 10 equals 15, and $15 − 10 = 5$ is 15 minus 10 equals 5.

- Now you try it with $9 + 4 = 13$.

- What is 459 + 10? 459 + 100?

- What is 459 − 10? 459 − 100?

Repeat each activity several times.

Give the children some numbers, say 125, 80 and 231, and tell them they are going to try to make these numbers using + and − (for example, $80 = 30 + 30 + 20$). They can then make up their own 2- or 3-digit numbers for which they write similar number statements using only + and −.

- Which numbers did you try to make? How did you work them out?

- Would it make any difference if you added in a different order?

Teaching Input 5

- Can you double 24? Double 26? Double 25?

- Which tens number is closest to 14? To 56? To 78? To 21? To 91? And to 99?

- How many do you add to 154 to make 160?

- How many do you add to 1154 to make 1160?

- Which three numbers could you add to make 20? 33? 46? 29? 18?

number cards (1 to 9), paper and pencils

Ask the children to play the game 'Highest number wins', a game for two or more players (although it is preferable to play in pairs).

Shuffle the cards and place them face down. Ask one child in each pair to select four cards, turn them over and place them face up in the order in which they selected them. They and their partner must use + and = once each to make a number. Ask them to use each digit once only, and in the order in which the cards lie. For example, if they pick 6, 7, 3 and 5 they might say $673 + 5 = 678$, $6 + 735 = 741$ and so on. They should make sure their partner cannot see their working out. The winner each time is the player with the highest number.

- Can you explain what you have been doing? Did you find any patterns?

- How did you make sure you tried all the combinations?

Money and Real Life Problems, Making Decisions and Checking Results

This week we will be investigating and solving money problems, finding totals and giving change.

OBJECTIVES

- To solve word problems involving numbers in real life using one or more steps.
- To use £.p notation and convert from pence to pounds and vice versa.

LANGUAGE

operation, sequence

RESOURCES

Pupils' Book pages 16 and 17, PCM 15.

Teaching Input 1

- What is 65 + 11? Is there a different way to write that?

Repeat several times.

- What is 2 × 5? 5 × 2? 10 × 2? 2 × 10?
- What is 2 × 6? 2 × 8? 2 × 10? And 2 × 20?
- What is 6 × 2? 8 × 2? 10 × 2? And 20 × 2?

Repeat several times.

- Can you tell me any rules about multiplication? What about for addition?
- If I go into a cinema and buy two tickets costing £1.25 each, how much do I spend altogether?
- If I buy two ice creams costing 70p each, how much do I spend?
- If I buy two comics costing 90p each, how much do I spend?

Pupils' Book page 16

Ask the children to complete the work in the Pupils' Book in which they work out how much each alien must spend on jellybeans to reach the seaside.

- How much does each alien have to pay to get to the sea? If the aliens start off with £10, how much money will Zig have left? Zag have left? Zog have left? Which is the cheapest route and which is the most expensive?

Teaching Input 2

- If one spider has eight legs, how many legs will five spiders have? How many will ten spiders have? Two spiders? Four spiders?
- If I have 20 eggs in one basket, 15 in another and 28 in a third basket, how many eggs have I altogether?
- If I have five boxes that will each take 12 eggs, can I fit all the eggs in? Will there be any left over?
- If I think of a number, halve it and add 5, the answer is 27. What was my number?
- How many pence are there in £6.75? £3.21? £4.06? £5.01?
- How many pounds and pence are there in 734p? 322p? 407p? 502p?

Repeat several times.

Pupils' Book page 17

Ask the children to complete the exercise in the Pupils' Book, working out how much rides at a funfair cost and how much money they will have left.

Teaching Input 3

- If it costs £1.50 to go swimming, how much would it cost for two people to go? How much would it cost for three, five and ten people?

- Which three coins could make 60p? 80p? £1.55? 75p?

Repeat several times.

- I buy three stamps costing 20p and two costing 15p. How much did they cost altogether? If I gave a £2 coin for the stamps, how much change did I receive?

Repeat similar questions.

- How many pence are there in £10.07? In £6.51? In £2.50?

- How many pence are there in £8.43?

- What about £15.07 and £16.16?

PCM 15

Ask the children to complete the route to find out how much money they will end up with, starting from £5.

Teaching Input 4

- Can you share 20 sweets equally between two children, five children and ten children? How many does each child get?

Repeat several times.

- If I have £1 and I spend 23p, how much change do I get?

- If I have £1.50 and I spend 15p, how much change will I be given?

- If I have 65p in my purse and I have spent 35p, how much money did I have originally?

- What is 321 + 100 + 4? 461 + 100 + 5? 461 − 100 + 5? 461 − 100 + 4?

Repeat the activity several times.

- I have six eggboxes each containing four eggs, and three boxes each containing five eggs. How many eggs have I altogether? If each eggbox holds six eggs, how many more eggs would be needed to fill all the boxes?

Ask the children to copy out a similar template to PCM 15, in which there are 16 empty circles connected by arrows. (You may prefer to blank out the numbers and photocopy it.) Suggest a start amount and decide the rules (or you might suggest they start and finish with the same amounts). The children work their way along the pathway, writing the arrow rules and filling in the numbers.

- Tell me about your work? How easy was it to write the arrow instructions? Are there any patterns or rules? How might you change the rules?

Teaching Input 5

- How might you write three hundred and twenty-one pence differently?

- How might you write two hundred and fifteen pence differently?

- What about six hundred and five pence?

- Suggest how you might write £2.64 another way.

- What about £5.97 or £1.22?

Repeat several times.

- Add 70p + 30p + 92p.

- Now try 75p + 25p + £1.

- Add 80p + 25p + 73p.

- What is the total of 60p + 90p + £1.22?

Repeat several times.

- Two puzzles cost £3. How much does one puzzle cost?

Repeat with similar questions.

Tell the children that Auntie gives each of her nieces and nephews four coins. Sometimes they are all different, sometimes they are all the same. They could be any coin.

- What could they be worth? How much could each child have? Can you see any patterns?

- Do you think you found all the combinations? Can you see any patterns?

- Did you work to a formula? Has anyone got anything different? What was the highest total? The lowest total?

Measures and Time, including Problems

This week we will be doing quite a bit of practical work with just a minimum of recording. We will be reading scales and estimating measurements to the nearest whole or half unit.

Teaching Input 1

- My lunch went into the oven at 12:10 and it was cooked in 30 minutes. What time was it cooked?
- My dinner went into the oven at 5:30 and took 45 minutes to cook. What time was it ready?

Repeat several times.

- If I leave for school at 8:30 and it takes 20 minutes to walk, what time do I get there?

Repeat with similar questions.

- What is the difference in length between two ribbons, one of which is 23cm long and the other 76cm long?
- How many centimetres are there in one metre?
- How many metres are there in one kilometre?
- How many grams are there in one kilogram?
- How many litres are there in one millilitre?

Pupils' Book page 18, rulers

Ask the children to measure the parts of the UFO in the Pupils' Book, reminding them to measure twice to check their results.

- Does your length sound reasonable? Now draw some of your own lines and measure them, recording your answers.

Teaching Input 2

- What is a good unit to measure the width of the playground?
- What is a good unit to measure the distance between school and home?
- What might you use to measure the width of a desk or table?
- What about the height of a chair?
- Suggest a sensible unit to measure how tall you are.
- What is a good unit to measure how much a teapot holds?
- How might you measure how much a cup holds?
- What might you use to measure how much an eggcup holds?
- How many seconds are there in a minute?
- How many minutes are there in an hour?
- How many hours are there in a day?
- How many days are there in a week?
- How many weeks are there in a year?
- Tell me the 12 months of the year.

rulers, PCM 16, card, pencils, scissors, glue

Ask the children to use the PCM to make a box out of card.

- Does your box work? Are all the sides straight and at right angles to each other?

Teaching Input 3

 digital clock

- What do you think would take five minutes to do? What would take about 30 minutes? Or one hour? Or one week?

Show the class a digital clock.

- What time does this say?
- What would it be on an analogue clock? *For example, quarter past nine or fifteen minutes past nine.*
- How many days are there in a year?
- How many weeks are there in a year?
- How many days are there in a month? Are they all the same?

 rulers, objects to measure (both more and less than 1 metre)

Ask the children to work in pairs to find three things that measure between 5 and 30 centimetres.

- Check your objects by measuring. Were you right?

Teaching Input 4

- What do you think would weigh 10 grams, 100 grams and 1 kilogram? *For example, a bag of potatoes.*

If possible, check the children's suggestions by weighing.

 Pupils' Book page 19

Give the children the Pupils' Book page to complete by working out the amounts shown in the jugs.

Teaching Input 5

 sand or water, jugs, beakers

- Find a container that holds less than a cup or beaker.
- Find a container that holds more than a cup or beaker.

 Give the children some unmarked containers. Then specify how much the container is to hold. The child then tries to mark the container at the specified level and fills it with that amount of sand or water to see if they were right. They should record their findings.

Shape and Space

This week we are working on 2D and 3D shapes, including angles, turns and right angles. There will be quite a lot of practical work followed by discussion.

OBJECTIVES

- To describe and classify 2D and 3D shapes according to their properties.
- To make and describe 3D shapes.
- To identify right angles in 2D shapes and in the environment.
- To understand angle as a measure of turn.

LANGUAGE

angle, right angle, measurement of turn • vertices, edges, faces • properties, parallel • quadrilateral, circle, triangle, hexagon, octagon, pentagon • cubes, cuboid, prisms, cylinders, cones, triangular prism, hexagonal prism, sphere, hemisphere

RESOURCES

Selection of 2D and 3D shapes (including prisms and pyramids), square dotted paper (with the dots about 1cm apart), sheets of paper, interlocking cubes.

Teaching Input 1

 selection of 2D and 3D shapes

Show the children the 2D shapes.

- Tell me the names of these shapes.
- Now tell me what half a circle is called.
- Which shape has five sides?
- Which has four sides which are unequal in length?
- Tell me a shape that has one curved edge.
- Which shape has six straight sides?
- What can you tell me about quadrilaterals?
- How many sides does a triangle have? What about a square? A rectangle? A hexagon? An octagon? A pentagon?
- Can you name any quadrilaterals? *Write these down as they are mentioned: they may include square, rectangle, rhombus, parallelogram, trapezium and kite.*

Now show the children the 3D shapes. Ask them to sort them according to their properties, for instance, curved edges, triangular faces, shapes like boxes.

- How many corners do they have? How many vertices? *Explain that they both mean the same.*
- How many faces and edges?
- What is a sphere?
- What is a hemisphere?
- What can you tell me about the flat face of a hemisphere?

 square dotted paper, 2D shapes

Give the children a selection of 2D shapes with straight sides and ask them to sort them into two sets: quadrilaterals and not quadrilaterals. Then ask them to use the grid paper to draw as many quadrilaterals as they can, labelling them, where possible.

Note: It may help to discuss the names and properties of quadrilaterals, for example, a rhombus has four equal sides with the opposite sides parallel. Go on to describe other forms, such as the parallelogram.

If there is time, repeat the activity using 3D shapes.

- Can you tell me the names of your 4-sided shapes?
- What do we call all 4-sided shapes?

Teaching Input 2

- What do we mean by an angle?
- It is a measure of turn and the angle between two lines is how much you need to turn one line to match up with the other.

- It does not matter which line you turn, but it does matter which way you turn. Right angles are quarter turns.

Note: By this stage, children should have experienced quarter turns in PE. Make sure they understand that once they have turned through two quarter turns, they are facing the opposite direction and that they have to go through two more quarter turns to face the front again.

 selection of 3D shapes, sheets of paper

- How can we check right angles in the classroom?

- Fold a sheet of paper in half and then half again and you will have right angles. Using this right angle corner, you can find right angles in the classroom.

- Where can you find right angles in the classroom?

Give the children a selection of flat shapes and ask them to sort the shapes into three sets:

All right angles   No right angles   One or some right angles

Teaching Input 3

 selection of 2D and 3D shapes, interlocking cubes

Recap on 2D shapes by asking each child in the group to give their properties (for

instance, square: straight sides all equal, four vertices and four right angles). Then review 3D shapes by discussing their faces, vertices, edges, and any other properties they have.

- How many different shapes can you make with four interlocking cubes (mirror images are acceptable)?

These two are not duplicates, they are mirror images:

 - Now try to make a cube using some of these shapes (without breaking them or changing them). You will also need a shape made of three interlocking cubes in an L-shape. *One of the 'mirror image' shapes and the 4 × 1 shape will not be needed.*

Offer them a hint of a 3 × 3 × 3 cube.

- Use the cubes in three different colours to make a large solid cube, for example, using nine red, nine blue and nine green cubes to make each face show three red, three blue and three green cubes. Have fun!

- If you found that easy, try to make a cube with a different number of blue cubes on each face.

- Finally, make a cube according to your own rules.

 - What have you been doing? What did you discover? Did you use the extra shape?

- Which shapes did you leave out? Why? Did anyone use any different shapes?

- What about a 4 × 4 × 4 cube? Would the rules be different?

Reasoning about Shapes and Space

This week we are going to solve problems connected with patterns and recognise line symmetry.

Teaching Input 1

- Can you tell me a rule about odd numbers?
- What about a rule about even numbers?
- What happens when you add an odd and an even number?
- What happens when you add two odd numbers and an even number?
- What about when you add two even numbers and one odd number?
- Which odd numbers come between 68 and 80?
- Can you give me the odd numbers between 11 and 21?
- Tell me the odd numbers between 13 and 17.
- Which odd numbers come between 109 and 115?

Repeat several times.

- Now tell me the even numbers between 50 and 60.
- What about between 66 and 80?
- Tell me the even numbers between 100 and 110.
- What do I mean by a symmetrical pattern?
- What is meant by line symmetry? *It means a 'mirror' line – if you put a mirror along the shape it looks the same as without the mirror.*

 squared paper

Ask the children to draw some regular (symmetrical) and irregular shapes on their squared paper, making sure they are not crowded together. Show them how to draw in the line of symmetry in the regular shapes and encourage them to colour in the squares in one half in a pattern. They should then colour in the other half to make the shape and pattern symmetrical. For the irregular examples, the children need to complete the mirror image of the shape, and if they want to colour them in, they must make certain that the shape is symmetrical in both outline and pattern.

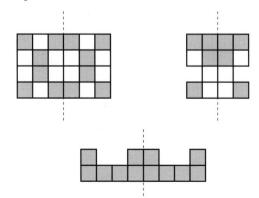

Teaching Input 2

- If you use the numbers 2, 3 and 5, and the signs × and +, what numbers could you make? Are there any numbers you can make in different ways? Write down your sums on a piece of paper. *For example,* $2 + 2 + 2 = 6, 3 + 3 = 6$ and $2 \times 3 = 6$.
- If you throw two dice, what numbers could you make? Write down your sums. *For example,* 2×6 or $2 + 6$.
- What is double 20? Double 30? Double 40? Double 50? Double 100?
- What is half of 20? Of 30? Of 40? Of 50? Of 100?

squared paper

Ask the children to colour in some symmetrical patterns on their paper, marking the line of symmetry in each case. Then write the capital alphabet on the board, making sure those letters which are symmetrical are very clear: A B C D E F G H I J K L M N O P Q R S T U V W X Y Z. Ask the children to copy the letters in their books and to draw in the lines of symmetry with dotted lines.

- Can you think of any numbers which are symmetrical?

Teaching Input 3

- Tell me some multiples of 10.
- Give me some numbers which are multiples of 5.
- Can you tell me some numbers that are multiples of 2?
- Can you give me a rule about symmetrical patterns?
- Can you tell me a letter that is symmetrical? Where is its line of symmetry?

PCM 17, scissors, glue

- Cut out the small, patterned squares carefully (do not lose any) and place them onto your quilt to make a symmetrical pattern. When you are happy with your arrangement, stick your squares down.
- Remember, if you decide to colour in the squares, the quilt must still be symmetrical.

- Did you manage to keep the quilt symmetrical? What patterns did you make?

Counting and Properties of Number, Reasoning about Numbers

This week we will be counting on and back in tens and hundreds from any 2-digit number, solving puzzles and problems involving numbers and explaining the work.

- To count on or back in tens or hundreds from any 2- or 3-digit number.
- To recognise odd and even numbers to 100.
- To investigate patterns and relationships, generalise, predict and explain.

LANGUAGE

multiple • sequence

RESOURCES

Dice (1 to 6), PCM 18, dominoes, paper, pencils, Pupils' Book pages 20 and 21, matchsticks.

Teaching Input 1

- Count on in twos to 50, and back.

- Now count on in tens to 110, and back.

- This time start at 33 and count in tens to 103.

- Now go from 49 and count on in hundreds to 949.

- How many hundreds, tens and units are there in 672? In 414? In 309? In 517? And in 888?

Repeat several times.

- Tell me the odd numbers between 70 and 82.

- Which are the odd numbers between 17 and 31?

- Tell me the even numbers between 73 and 81.

- Which even numbers come between 153 and 161?

- Which even number comes after 72? And 50? And 34? And 30?

- Count on in twos from 12 to 30 and from 152 to 170.

- Count on in threes from 15 to 30 and from 24 to 39.

dice (1 to 6)

Tell the children they are going to play the 'Dice game'. Put the children in groups of four and give each group a dice. Before the game starts, each group should decide if the highest score wins, the lowest score wins, the score nearest 100 wins, or another rule. Then, in turn, each child throws the dice and all four children write down the score in their own books. Once all four numbers have been written down in a row, each child must write $+$, $-$, $\times$ or $\div$ between each number in their books (making sure the rest of the group can't see!). Remind the groups that they can use any sign as often as they like and in any order. They then work out their calculation to see who has won that round.

Teaching Input 2

- Continue the pattern 5, 10, 15 … to 50.

- Continue the pattern 4, 8, 12 … to 48. What is the pattern?

Ask each child in turn to start their own sequence and ask the other children to explain it. Were they correct?

- Tell me the rules for the following:

    Multiples of 10 end in …?

    Multiples of 5 end in …?

Multiples of 2 end in …?

Multiples of 100 end in …?

Multiples of 50 end in …?.

- Which of the numbers 2, 4, 6, 8, 9, 11, 12, 14 and 16 are not multiples of 2?

- Count on in fifties to 1000, and back.

PCM 18

Ask the children to complete the PCM, in which they choose numbers on a number square and count on in fives.

- What can you tell me about the square?

- What patterns can you see?

- How many number jumps are needed to land on 100? And 110? And 121?

Teaching Input 3

- Tell me three numbers which add up to 20. Are there any others?

- Now tell me three numbers which add up to 35? Is that the only solution?

- Can you tell me two numbers which, when multiplied together, make 20? Are there any others? *For example, 4 × 5, 5 × 4, 2 × 10, 10 × 2.*

- Suggest two numbers which, multiplied together, make 24.

Repeat several times.

- If I have 12 sweets to share out equally among three children, how many sweets would each child get?

- What about 12 sweets and two children? Or 12 sweets and four children? Or 12 sweets and six children?

- What are 20 × 2 and 25 × 2? How did you solve that?

Repeat with similar questions.

dominoes, paper, pencils, Pupils' Book page 20

Ask the children to complete the 'Target game' in the Pupils' Book in which they use five dominoes to make a target number using +, −, × and ÷.

- Did you reach all your targets? Could you have used those numbers in a different way to get that total?

Teaching Input 4

- What is half of 10? Of 12? Of 14? Of 20? Of 30? Of 40? Of 50? Of 60? Of 100?

- Can you give me a rule about odd or even numbers?

- Can you give me a rule about triangles, squares, rectangles and hexagons?

- How many ways can you make 30 using 2, 3, 5 and 6? You may use each number as many times as you like. Write down all the possibilities. Have you used +, −, × and ÷?

Give the children a variety of calculations to complete, such as: 100 ÷ 2, 50 + 70 + 9 + 5, 100 + 97, 200 + 54 + 60, 80 ÷ 2, 364 + 100 + 22, 525 − 100 − 100, 707 − 100 + 50, £1.50 + £1.50, 174 − 74, 274 − 100, 20 × 2, 20 × 10, 20 × 5.

Teaching Input 5

dice (1 to 6)

- How many do I add to 50 to make 76?

- How many do I add to 24 to make 29?

- How many do I add to 110 to make 120?

Give the children two, three or four dice and ask them to take turns to make totals with the numbers they throw. They should write these down as they are calculated. Have they used +, −, × and ÷ to make their totals?

Pupils' Book page 21, matchsticks

Put the children in pairs to play 'Matchsticks', as described in the Pupils' Book, giving each pair 24 sticks. When they have completed a task, such as making 5 squares with their matchsticks, they should either show it to you or record it on a sheet of paper. So with 15 sticks, they might make two large and two small squares.

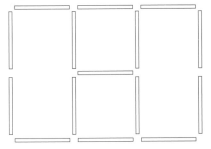

Understanding + and −, Mental Calculation Strategies

This week we will be extending addition and subtraction using larger numbers, and developing mental strategies.

OBJECTIVES

- To add three 2-digit numbers.
- To use knowledge that numbers can be added in any order and to do mental calculations more efficiently.
- To find, describe and use patterns of similar calculations.
- To extend understanding that subtraction is the inverse of addition.

LANGUAGE

addition, subtraction, operation, add on • operators +, −, = • patterns, possibilities

RESOURCES

PCMs 19, 20 and 21.

Teaching Input 1

- What is 94 + 10? 94 + 100? 80 plus 50? 60 plus 32? 73 plus 10?
- What is 32 + 9? 32 + 11? 46 + 9? 46 + 11? How did you work them out?
- If I add 50p to £1.25, how much would I have altogether?
- Which two numbers could add up to 27? Are there any others?
- Which two numbers could add up to 59? Can anyone think of some more combinations?
- If I think of a number and add 30 to it, it makes 75. What was my number?
- Can you tell me three numbers which add up to 19?
- What about three numbers which add up to 62?
- Or three numbers which add up to 109?

Repeat several times.

 Give the children some target numbers, say 155, 250, 300, 100 and 99, and challenge them to write eight calculation sentences to make each target. Tell them that they may only use the operations + and −, for instance, 155 = 50 + 50 + 55.

Teaching Input 2

- How might we write 96 + 30 differently and get the same answer?
- What is 220 + 132? What is the answer if we reverse it to say 132 + 220?
- Add together 20 + 25 + 25.
- Now add 30 + 25 + 25.
- What is 12 + 17 + 13? How did you work out the answer?

Repeat several times.

- What about 12 + 13 + 14? How did you solve it?
- Can you tell me three numbers which will add up to 20? To 30? To 63? To 101?

Repeat the activity with different calculations.

 Tell the children that they are going to play 'Explode 19'. The aim of the game is to reduce 3- and 4-digit numbers down to 19 using only the operations +, − and =. They can, however, use any number or operation as often as necessary. For example 2000 − 1981 = 19 or 100 − 80 − 1 = 19 or 100 − 91 + 10 = 19.

- How difficult was it to use only the two operations?

- Did you find all the possibilities?
- How many different ways did you find of doing this?
- What have other people got?
- Have you used any patterns?

Teaching Input 3

- Take 6 away from 12.
- What is 18 subtract 6?
- Take 6 away from 29.
- What is 55 subtract 9?
- What is 55 subtract 11?
- If I add 8 to 52, what is the answer?
- If I add 9 to 56, what is the answer?
- Add 7 + 8 + 12.
- What is 15 + 15 + 22?
- Tell me the answer to 12 + 12 + 12.
- What is 23 + 17 + 0?
- Add 37 + 52 and 36 + 63. Explain how you worked them both out.
- What is 506 − 498? How do you find the answer?

Continue asking addition and subtraction questions with examples where it is advisable to add on, for example, 88 − 79, and 109 − 102.

PCM 19

Give the PCMs to the children for them to 'Find the totals', in which they are looking for numbers which total 25 and 125 on the table.

Teaching Input 4

- If 3 + 9 = 12, what does 30 + 90 equal?
- If 4 + 9 = 13, what does 40 + 90 equal?

Continue with other examples.

- Can each of you suggest a similar pattern to me?

- What is 274 − 9? How did you work it out? Did you come up with 265 because 274 − 10 = 264 (+ 1) = 265? Can you give me another similar example? And another one?
- What is 32 + 15? Can you write that in a different way?

Repeat several times.

- What is 80 + 25? And 60 + 76?
- What do I add to 70 to make 140? To make 150? To make 200?

PCM 20

Hand out the PCM and ask the children to choose their own starting number to put through the flow chart.

- What do you notice about the diagonal arrows?

Teaching Input 5

- What is 30 + 40? 70 + 30? 90 + 50? 90 + 40?

Repeat several times.

- What is 112 − 100? 112 − 12? 100 − 50? 100 − 70?

Repeat several times.

- What about 316 + 100? 443 + 100?
- How many do I add to 70 to make 130?
- How many do I add to 666 to make 700?
- How many do I add to 666 to make 766?
- Work out 57 + 7, 63 + 11 and 45 + 8. How did you find the answers?

Repeat with similar questions.

PCM 21

Ask the children to complete the 'See-saw' PCM by making the two sides balance.

Understanding × and ÷, Money and Real Life Problems

This week we will be solving problems using multiplication and division, and using pounds and pence.

OBJECTIVES

- To recognise all coins, find totals and give change.
- To use all four operations as appropriate to solve real life problems.
- To extend understanding that multiplication can be done in any order.
- To understand that division is the inverse of multiplication.

LANGUAGE

multiplication, division, ×, ÷ • pounds, pence, £ notation, p notation • half, share between • cost

RESOURCES

Pupils' Book pages 22, 23 and 24, PCM 22, coins, counters.

Teaching Input 1

- What is 2 × 10? And 10 × 2? And 2 × 5? And 5 × 2? And 3 × 3? And 3 × 5? And 5 × 3?
- What is double 2? Double 5? Double 10?
- What is half of 10? Half 12? Half 16? Half 18? Half 20? Half 50? Half 100?
- If I have ten balloons and share them equally between ten children, how many balloons will each child receive? What if I share them among five children? Or two children?
- If I have 20 apples and share them equally between two children, how many apples will each child receive? How many would five children receive? What about four children? And ten children?

Pupils' Book page 22, PCM 22, coins

Ask the children to play the 'Make that' game, using the instructions in the Pupils' Book and the cards cut from the PCM. The aim is to work through all 20 cards, making money statements for each one. For example, if a player turns over £1, they might make it with 50p + 50p while their partner might choose 50p + 20p + 20p + 10p. They should keep making the same total until one player cannot find another way, when this happens, the turn passes to their partner who takes another card.

Teaching Input 2

counters

You may use counters to demonstrate the first part, if necessary.

- What is 16 ÷ 4? 20 ÷ 5? 18 ÷ 2? 18 ÷ 9? 26 ÷ 2? 24 ÷ 6? And 30 ÷ 5?

Repeat the activity several times.

- If you have £50 and theatre tickets cost £10 each, how many can you buy?
- If the tickets cost £2, how many could you buy with your £50? How many could you buy if they cost £5?
- How many pence are there in £3.60?
- How many pence are there in £4.85?
- How many pounds and pence are there in 837p? In 946p? In 332p?

Repeat this activity.

Pupils' Book page 23

Ask the children to complete the 'Stamps' exercise in the Pupils' Book by investigating different combinations of amounts.

Teaching Input 3

Write four mathematical statements on the board, for example,

5 × 6 = 30 and 30 ÷ 6 = 5

6 × 5 = 30 and 30 ÷ 5 = 6

- What do you notice about these four calculations?

- Can each of you give me similar sums and sentences? Use the numbers 2, 5 and 10.

- If you know $4 \times 5 = 20$, what is 5×4? What is $20 \div 4$? And $20 \div 5$?

Repeat several times.

- What is 6×10? And 6×100? What about 7×10? And 7×100? Now try $70 \div 10$. And $700 \div 100$.

Repeat the activity.

 counters

Draw the following on the board and ask the children to copy it into their books.

12	7	9	30	6
16	5	2	3	27
1	21	10	45	18
6	40	8	15	35
14	24	4	16	20

Tell them to choose two numbers between 1 and 9. They then use × and ÷ to try to make one of the numbers on the grid. If they can, they cover it with a counter. The first to make three in a row, horizontally, vertically or diagonally is the winner. Later, the children can try playing the game making four in a row.

Teaching Input 4

- How many pence are there in £4.10? £6.72? £9.47? £9.99? £10?

Repeat several times.

- How many pounds and pence are there in 943p? 999p? 601p? 702p?

- If you have ten one pound coins and 83 pennies, how much is that in pounds and pence?

- I have £3 and I spend 30p on a chocolate bar, 60p on a comic and 50p on two lollipops. How much did I spend and how much money have I left?

- I spent 75p, then 30p, then £1. How much did I spend altogether?

Repeat several times.

 Pupils' Book page 24

Tell the children to work through the questions on the 'Stationery shop', working out how much each customer will have left.

Teaching Input 5

- If I have three silver coins, how much money might I have? How much would they each be worth?

- My bill is £1.54. What coins could I use to pay it?

Repeat several times.

- If one ladybird has 12 spots, how many do two ladybirds have?

- If a spider has eight legs, how many legs are there on two spiders? Three spiders? Ten spiders?

Repeat the activity.

- How would you work out 32×2? $30 + 39$? 35×2? 25×2? Did anyone do them differently?

Repeat several times.

 Ask the children to make up number sentences using some of the numbers and signs shown.

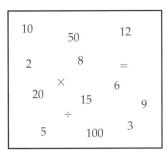

- What can you discover?

- What happened in your calculations? What do we mean by dividing?

- Have you found all the possibilities? How many different ways can you find of doing this?

Fractions

This week we are working on fractions, recognising that a fraction is a part of whole and comparing familiar fractions.

Teaching Input 1

- What do we mean by a fraction?
- What is half of 2? Of 3? Of 4? Of 30?
- What is double 15? Double 13? Double 9? Double 7? Double 5? Double 3? Double 1?
- What happens if you double an even number? An odd number?
- What happens when you halve an even number?
- If I divide a cake into quarters, how many pieces are there?
- If I divide a cake equally among eight people, how much will each get?
- How many quarters do I add to one quarter to make one whole? To make three quarters?

interlocking cubes

Working in pairs, using cubes in two colours, ask the children to pick out 20 and make a shape that is half red and half blue. Now ask them to take another 20 cubes and make another shape that is quarter red and three quarters blue. Now ask them to choose another 20 cubes and make a shape that is quarter blue and three quarters red. Finally, the children should take sets of 20 cubes and make shapes that are one tenth red and nine tenths blue, two tenths red and eight tenths blue, then three tenths red and seven tenths blue.

- Show me your 'half and half' shapes. How many cubes of each colour are there? Has anyone constructed their 'half and half' shape in a different way? How about the shape that is quarter red and three quarters blue? Does anyone have another shape? What have you discovered about how many red and blue cubes there are in the shapes?

Repeat the discussion for the other fraction shapes the children have made.

Teaching Input 2

1–100 number line

- What is another way of writing the fractions $\frac{3}{6}$, $\frac{4}{8}$, $\frac{5}{10}$ and $\frac{1}{2}$? Can you tell me any other halves? For example $\frac{10}{20}$.
- What is half of 4? Of 6? Of 8? Of 30?
- What is half of 7? Of 9? Of 5?
- Look at the number line. Which number is halfway between 0 and 20?
- Which is halfway between 20 and 40?
- What about halfway between 40 and 60?

Draw a 1–5 number line on the board, marking in the halfway points.

```
1       2       3       4       5
|---|---|---|---|---|---|---|---|
```

- Which number is halfway between 1 and 2?
- Which is halfway between 2 and 3?

Repeat several times.

PCM 23

Ask the children, in pairs or small groups, to play 'Snap!' using two sets of the fraction cards cut from the PCM.

Teaching Input 3

- What is another way of writing $\frac{5}{10}$? $\frac{3}{6}$? $\frac{2}{4}$? $\frac{10}{20}$? $\frac{50}{100}$? $\frac{4}{8}$?
- What is half of 12? 15? 18? 22? 26?

Repeat several times.

- If I divide my bar of chocolate between four people, how much will each person receive?
- If I give away one tenth of my sweets, what fraction have I left?
- If I have ten sweets and I give away two tenths, how many are left? What if I give away five tenths or one half?
- Which number is halfway between 7 and 8? 12 and 13? 12 and 14?

Repeat this activity.

square dotted paper, coloured pens

Begin by drawing a dotted grid on the board, about 10 × 10 dots. Then join some dots to form a shape and colour in a fraction using two colours. For example, $\frac{1}{2}$:

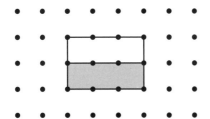

Now ask the children to draw four shapes and to colour them:

1. half red and half blue
2. quarter blue and three quarters red
3. one tenth red and nine tenths blue
4. two eighths red and six eighths blue.

Then ask them to write down how many red and how many blue squares there are in each picture.

- In each section, what fraction was each colour? How many sections were coloured red and how many were blue? Is $\frac{13}{26}$ a half? Are you sure? How do you know?

Teaching Input 4

- What is one tenth of 10? Of 20? Of 30?
- What is quarter of 4? Of 8? Of 16? Of 20?
- What is half of 20? 50? 30? 70? And 90?
- What is one third of 3? Of 6? Of 9? And of 12?
- How much do I add to one third to make one whole?
- How much do I add to one half to make one whole?
- How much do I add to six eighths to make one whole?

Pupils' Book page 25

Ask the children to work through the fractions revision exercises in the Pupils' Book.

- Could you work out all the fractions? How did you work them out?
- Did anyone work differently?

Teaching Input 5

- Which is the greater, half or quarter?
- Which is the greater, half or three quarters?
- Which is the greater, two tenths or five tenths?
- Which is the greater, four eighths or six eighths?

Repeat several times.

- Each of you now ask the others a fraction question, for example, what is a different way of writing five tenths?
- Which number is halfway between 9 and 10?
- What lies halfway between 21 and 22?

Repeat with similar questions.

Pupils' Book page 26

The children will be working out proportions of ingredients in some recipes.

- How did you halve the recipes? Was it easy? When might you want to halve a recipe?
- What amounts did you get when you doubled the ingredients? When might you need to do that?

Handling Data

This week we will be handling data by collecting, sorting and organising information.

Teaching Input 1

large sheets of paper

- Do you know what we mean by a Venn diagram?
- Do you know what we mean by a Carroll diagram?

Draw some examples on a large sheet of paper for the children to see.

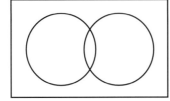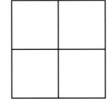

- I have heard that most boys' names start with one of the letters that come after 'H' in the alphabet. How might we prove that?
- How could we collect the information and sort it out?
- How could we display it for others to see?

Ask the children to work in pairs and provide them with the following instructions.

1. Make a list of all the children in the class and indicate if their names start with a letter after 'H' or not. For example:

Names	After 'H'	Not after 'H'
Frank		Y
Sanjay	Y	
Mary	Y	

2. Then draw a Venn diagram on a large sheet of paper, and transfer the information.

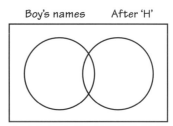

Boy's names   After 'H'

- Where do you put the information that does not fit into the circles?

Discuss the Venn diagram.

- What did you put in each circle?
- What did you put outside the circle?

Teaching Input 2

- What is a Carroll diagram?
- What are they used for?
- Can you remember what they look like?

Draw a Carroll diagram on a large sheet of paper.

	Boys	Girls
Initials of names after H		
Initials of names not after H		

Ask the children to copy out the Carroll diagram and to use the list and Venn diagram from the previous session to fill it in. Remind them to make sure they do not leave anyone out.

- How can you ensure that you have included everyone?
- Make sure you put everyone in the right area.

Teaching Input 3

Return to the Carroll and Venn diagrams created in the earlier teaching sessions.

- Did you find out if most names started with letters after 'H'?
- How many boys' names were not after 'H'? How many were after 'H'?
- How many girls' names were not after 'H'? How many were after 'H'?
- Do you think it was a fair selection?
- What do you think the results would be if you asked the children in another class?

- What do you think the results would be if you asked the children in the whole school?
- Can you think of other ways to collect, organise and display information?
- Which was easier to interpret, the Venn diagram or the Carroll diagram?

Pupils' Book page 27

Ask the children to copy and complete the Venn and Carroll diagrams in the Pupils' Book.

- How many children were in your survey? Were there more girls than boys or more boys than girls?
- How many children had names with initials after 'H' and not after 'H'? Would the information be different if we asked more children? Do you think it was a fair test? In the Pupils' Book, how many numbers were a multiple of 3 and more than 30? How many numbers did not fit the circles?

Place Value, Ordering and Rounding

The work this week will be about reading and writing numbers in words and figures, ordering numbers, and rounding numbers to the nearest 10 or 100.

OBJECTIVES

- To round numbers to the nearest 10.
- To order whole numbers in words and figures.
- To read the vocabulary of comparing and ordering numbers.
- To identify which of a given set of numbers is nearest to another given number.

LANGUAGE

more than, less than • order, sets • round numbers

RESOURCES

PCMs 24 and 25, Pupils' Book pages 28, 29 and 30, packets, bottles, containers.

Teaching Input 1

PCMs 24 and 25

Place the 'larger than', 'smaller than', 'more than' and 'less than' cards spread well out on a table. Shuffle the cards with numbers on and words on, keeping them separate and put them in two piles, face down. The children, in turn, pick up one number and one word card and put them either side of the appropriate description card.

364

less than

five hundred

The child should read out what has been placed on the table as 'Three hundred and sixty-four is less than five hundred'.

Repeat until all the cards have been used.

Pupils' Book page 28

Ask the children to work through the number ordering exercise in the Pupils' Book.

- What patterns could you see? Did you check your work? Has everyone got the same results? Does anyone have something different?

Teaching Input 2

- Which number is 100 after 3? After 17? After 111? After 351? After 444? After 702 and after 900?

Repeat several times.

Play 'I am thinking of a number'. Give only a broad criterion to begin with, such as 'it lies between 50 and 200', and allow the children ten questions to work it out. For example, 'Is it an even number?' 'Is it less than 100?' 'Is it a multiple of 10?' 'Of 5?' 'Of 2?' It is helpful to photocopy an appropriate number grid for each child so they can cross off numbers as they are eliminated. This helps them to see which questions are most useful.

Repeat the game two or three times.

Pupils' Book pages 29 and 30

Ask the children to complete the 'Number keys' exercises in the Pupils' Book in which they must select first the nearest number and then the nearest ten to a given figure from a choice of three.

Teaching Input 3

 packets, bottles, containers

Ask the children, in turn, to read the amounts on the labels and to write the information down. They should then sort the information into sets, for instance, grams or millilitres, and order the sets from the smallest to the largest.

 Give the children a variety of numbers in numerals for them to rewrite in words, and numbers in words for them to rewrite in numerals. For example,

ten   one thousand five hundred and three

  9301   six hundred and ninety-six

8014   six thousand eight hundred and ninety

    5289   four thousand seven hundred and nineteen

2978   two thousand three hundred and eighty-six

   1014   nine hundred and fifty-six

Understanding + and −, Mental Calculation Strategies

This week we will be working on adding and subtracting, and understanding the related vocabulary. We will also focus on bridging through 10 or 100 or a multiple of 10 or 100.

OBJECTIVES

- To know and use addition and subtraction facts for each number to 20.
- To use informal pencil and paper procedures to add large sets of numbers.
- To identify doubles and near doubles of numbers up to 1000.

LANGUAGE

combination, addition, double • subtraction, difference • highest score, lowest score • calculation, techniques, strategies

RESOURCES

Dice, paper, pencils, Pupils' Book page 31, PCM 26.

Teaching Input 1

- What is 86 + 1073 + 9? 25 + 25? 29 + 31? 75 + 9? And 63 + 47? How did you work them all out? What techniques did you use?
- Can you give me two numbers which add up to 27? To 100? To 111? To 109? To 300 and to 302? Are those the only combinations?
- What is 33 − 9? 33 − 11?
- Subtract 35 from 70. Now try 25 from 50. What is 50 taken away from 100?

Repeat several times.

dice, paper, pencils

Tell the children they are going to play a game in pairs and hand out the equipment, giving each pair three dice. To play the game, the children throw the dice and write the scores down, for example, 5, 2, and 4.

They make a 2-digit number from the first two, and take away the last number, in this case, 52 − 4 = 48. This is repeated five times (or a number of times previously agreed) with the totals being added as they proceed. For example, 48 + 30 (36 − 6) = 78 + 61 (65 − 4) = 139 + … and so on.

The child with the highest score after five times wins.

Note: Care will be needed with this game, children must be confident how to play.

- Can you tell me about your game? What did you do? Was that the best way?
- Which was the most difficult bit?

Teaching Input 2

- What is double 30? Double 40? Double 50? Double 60? Double 70? Double 80? Double 90? Double 100? Double 150? Double 200 and double 250?
- Can you give me two numbers with a difference of 20? *For example*, 50 − 30 = 20.
- Can you give me two numbers with a difference of 30? Are there any more?
- Can you give me two numbers with a difference of 25?

Repeat several times.

- Subtract 15 from 45, 20 from 55, 25 from 100, and 75 from 100.

Repeat the activity.

- Work out 15 + 15 + 7 + 3. How did you find the answer?
- Work out 20 + 25 + 25 + 17 + 2. How did you calculate that?
- Continue the pattern: $8 + 1 = 9$

  $80 + 10 =$
- Now continue this: $22 + 6 = 28$

  $220 + 60 =$
- Calculate 80 + 20, 80 + 24 and 80 + 26.
- Work out 60 + 65 and 70 + 72.

Repeat several times.

Draw two millipedes on the board and ask the children to copy them in their books (or blank out PCM 32).

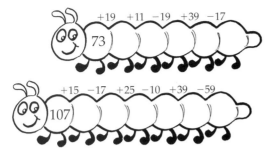

Then ask them to complete the chains by following the addition and subtraction instructions.

 • How did you calculate the first one? Was the second more difficult? Why? How did you overcome the problems?

Teaching Input 3

 • Tell me 100 + 64, 202 + 64, 402 + 25, 730 + 100 and 750 + 150. How did you work them out?

 • Now calculate 60 − 32, 66 − 33 and 96 − 72. How did you find the answers?

 • What do you add to 50 to make 100? What do you add to 70? 80? And 15?

 • What is 614 + 100? 614 − 100? 796 + 100? And 796 − 100?

Repeat several times.

 • What is 78 − 7? How did you do that?

 • What is 78 − 71? Is there another way of working it out?

Repeat the activity.

Pupils' Book page 31

Ask the children to complete the 'Snail paths' exercise in the Pupils' Book in which snails have to climb a wall from brick to brick (they cannot jump across bricks). The children investigate which snail gets the highest score.

 • What was the highest score? How did you get that?

 • What about the lowest score?

 • Did you check your workings? If so, how did you do that?

Teaching Input 4

 • How many do you add to 70 to reach 100? To 75? 95? 19? 35? 36? And 90? Have you any

suggestions how to do the calculations? Any suggestions to make it easier?

 • What is 1000 − 994? 900 − 890? 396 − 389?

Repeat this activity several times.

 • How did you work all those out? Did everyone use the same method?

 • What is 500 + 500? 500 + 700? 200 + 800? 200 + 97? 970 + 100? And 970 + 200? Explain what you have been doing. Do you have any helpful suggestions?

PCM 26

Hand out the PCM. Explain to the children that they add the five circle numbers and subtract the number in a square to find the total to put in the centre of the hexagon.

 • Did you add the smaller to the larger numbers? Does it matter in which order you add the numbers? Would it make any difference if the square was round another number?

Teaching Input 5

 • What is 695 − 1? 695 − 5? 695 − 95? 600 + 27? And 600 + 270?

Repeat the activity with similar questions.

 • Can you see any patterns?

 • Work out 55 + 50, 45 + 23 and 97 − 90.

 • What is 59 + 9? 59 + 11? 73 + 30? And 45 + 35? How did you work them out?

 • Can you give me three numbers which add up to 150? To 100? To 95? To 75?

Repeat several times.

 • What is 30 + 30? 35 + 35? 36 + 35? And 46 + 35?

Repeat several times.

Give the children the answer of 93 and tell them their challenge is to work out what the question might be! Tell them they may use +, − and = and to note their workings in their books, for example, 100 − 7 = 93 or 1000 − 907 = 93 or 50 + 43 = 93.

 • What did you do? What have you done so far? Did anyone do anything different?

Money and Real Life Problems

This week we are going to be working on money problems and investigations.

OBJECTIVES

- To use paper and pencil procedures to solve real life problems with more than one step.
- To use all four operations in the context of money.

LANGUAGE

amounts, costs, how much, bill • pounds, pence • change, mistakes, decimal notation

RESOURCES

Large sheet of paper, PCM 27, Pupils' Books pages 32 and 33, money (in various coins and notes).

Teaching Input 1

large sheet of paper

- What is 46 + 57 = ? How did you work it out?

Explain that it can be broken up to make it easier and write down:

$(40 + 50) + (6 + 7) = 90 + 13 = 90 + 10 + 3 = 103$

Point out that it can also be done as
$46 + 50 = 96 + 7 = 103$

Repeat and explain that tens units plus tens units equals tens plus tens plus units plus units. As you explain, write
$TU + TU = T + T + U + U$ on the board.

- What about 66 + 24? This could be done as $60 + 20 + 6 + 4 = 90$. Or as $6 + 4 = 10$ and $10 + 20 + 60 = 90$.

Repeat this activity until the children are confident with the method. Encourage each child to give you a number for a sum, write the sum down and show how it could be worked out.

- Now try the sums 57 + 24, 36 + 57 and 45 + 54.

Repeat this to give the children experience to develop their confidence.

PCM 27

Give the children the PCM to complete by following the 'money chain'. You might suggest they use a spare sheet of paper to work out their sums.

- What numbers did you end up with? Did everyone get the same?

Teaching Input 2

money

Point out to the children that if you write 50p on its own, you use the 'p' sign, and if you write it with the '£' sign you do not need to put the 'p' in. For example, £1.50 means £1 and 50p, or one pound fifty or one pound fifty pence – it all means the same.

Write £1.07 on the board. Tell the children this means one pound and seven pence – and that the decimal point separates the pounds and pence.

- How many pence are there in £3.64? £4.52?
- How many pounds and pence are there in 741p? 699p? 804p? And 115p?
- If you have £5 and you spend £3.50, how much change would you get?

Repeat with similar questions.

- If one book costs 25p, how much would four cost? Six? Ten?

money, Pupils' Book page 32

Ask the children to complete the fish and chips exercise, investigating costs and amounts of change. They might find it helpful to use real money to work some of it out.

Teaching Input 3

- Can you tell me why we put the decimal point between pounds and pence?

- How many pence are there in £10? £9.64? £7.21? £4.36? And £5.19?

- How many pounds and pence are there in 888p? 561p? 101p? 207p? 319p? And 729p?

Repeat several times.

- If one comic costs 50p, how much would three cost? Five cost? Ten cost? Two cost?

- I can save 50p every week. How long will I have to save to reach £3.50, £2.50 and £10?

Repeat this several times.

money, Pupils' Book page 33

Ask the children to complete the bills page in the Pupils' Book, using the money for help. Ray has had lots of complaints. Sometimes he copies the amounts incorrectly and sometimes he does not add up the totals correctly. Ask the children to sort them out.

- If each bill was paid with £10, how much change should the customers get? Did everyone get the same answers?

Teaching Input 4

- How much is 50p + 50p + 75p + 30p?

- How much is £1 + 75p + £1.25 + 40?

- What is £2 + £2 + £1.37?

- How much is 90p + 90p + 90p?

Repeat several times.

- If I want to buy a book for £3.75 and a pen for £1.00, how much money do I need altogether? If I paid with £5, how much change would I get?

- If it costs 75p for one person to go to the cinema, how much would it cost for two people to go? For three people? Four? Ten?

- I have £3 and my bill is £2.20. How much change do I get?

- I have £2 and my bill is £1.60. How much change do I get?

Repeat several times.

Pupils' Book page 32

Refer the children back to Ray's Fish and Chips in the Pupils' Book and ask them to work out the cost of:

1. two large portions of fish, two small portions of chips and one portion of peas
2. three fizzy drinks
3. one sausage, a small portion of chips and one portion of peas
4. one burger, a large portion of chips and one orange juice
5. one small ice cream and one large ice cream
6. one large portion of chips and a fizzy drink
7. two portions of fish fingers and two small portions of chips
8. one portion of fish fingers, a small portion of chips and one portion of peas.

Teaching Input 5

- I am thinking of a number. If I double it and add 12, the answer is 38. What was my number?

- If I have four eggboxes, each of which holds six eggs, how many eggs can I pack? What if I have ten boxes?

- If a handkerchief has nine spots, how many spots are there on two handkerchieves? Four handkerchieves? Five handkerchieves and ten handkerchieves?

- What is half of 100? 200? 500? 1000?

- What is 410 added to 100? 620 to 100? 1000 to 100? 246 + 300, 291 + 200 and 510 to 200?

Repeat several times.

Tell the children they have stamps which cost 20p and 15p.

- If I have £1, how many 15p stamps can I buy? Will I get any change?

- If I have £1, how many 20p stamps can I buy? Will I be given any change?

- If I have £2, can I buy eleven 20p stamps? How many can I buy and what change do I get?

- If I have £2 and I want to buy three 20p stamps and four 15p stamps, how much will they cost and what change will I get?

- How much would eight 20p stamps cost?

- How much would five 15p stamps and three 20p stamps cost altogether?

Measures, including Problems

This week we are going to be working on measures, including problems.

Teaching Input 1

- How many metres are there in one kilometre?
- How many grams are there in one kilogram?
- How many millilitres are there in a litre?
- Can you tell me what I mean by 3.5 metres? *For example, 3 metres 50 centimetres.*
- What do I mean by 6.8 metres? By 7.2 metres?
- What might I measure in kilometres? In metres? In centimetres? In kilograms? In grams? In litres? And in millilitres?

tape measures, rulers

Tell the children that today they are going to work in pairs to collect some information, and that they will continue to use the information tomorrow. Remind them to check and record the data carefully and to use the correct end of the tape measure.

Draw this table on the board and ask the children to copy it into their books. (Alternatively, you may prefer to photocopy it for them.)

| Object to measure | Your partner's name: | |
	Estimate	Measurement
Round your partner's wrist		
The length of your partner's foot		
Your partner's hand span		
Round your partner's head		
From their shoulder to wrist		
From their shoulder to floor		
From their knee to foot		
Your partner's height		

Ask the children to estimate the information about their partner, recording it in the table, then to use a ruler and tape measure to make the measurements. They should find this easier as they become more experienced. Remind them they will be using this table again tomorrow.

Teaching Input 2

- If I get up at 8am and leave for school at 8.45, how long do I have to get ready?
- If I get into the swimming pool at 2.45 and swim for 40 minutes, what time do I get out?

Repeat with similar questions.

- We go out for lunch at 12 noon and lunch lasts for 50 minutes. What time does it end?

Repeat several times.

- If I read from 2.10 until 3.00, how long do I read for?

large sheets of paper

Ask the children to get out the table they completed yesterday. Then, in groups, encourage them to compare, share and discuss the data. For this purpose, they will find it useful to copy everybody's information onto one large table so they have everyone's information on a single sheet. Draw the following model for them to copy onto a large sheet of paper.

Name	Round wrist	Length of foot	Hand span	Round the head	. Shoulder to wrist	Shoulder to floor	Knee to foot	Height

- Can you see any connection between height and shoulder to wrist measurement?
- Can you see any connection between the length of the foot and hand span?
- Is there anything else you can tell me from the information?

Teaching Input 3

- Can you think of something that is 1 centimetre long?
- Can you tell me something that is 10 centimetres long?
- Can you think of something that is 100 centimetres long?
- Can you think of something that is 2 metres long?
- What do you think might hold about 1 litre?
- What do you think would hold about half a litre?
- What do you think might weigh 1 kilogram?
- What do you think might weigh 5 kilograms?

scales and balances, selection of objects

Ask the children to copy this table into their books.

Object	Weighs more than	Weighs less than	Estimated weight	True weight

Then, as a group, encourage them to find and collect things that weigh between 100 grams and 1 kilogram. They should work in pairs to estimate and record their findings in the table.

- How accurate were your estimates? Did you tend to overestimate or underestimate?

Teaching Input 4

- How many days are there in a week?
- How many days are there in a month? Is it always the same?
- How many months are there in a year?
- How many seconds are there in a minute?
- How many minutes are there in an hour?
- How many hours are there in a day?
- When is your birthday? In which day, month and year were you born?

Pupils' Book page 34

Ask the children to answer the measures problems in their books.

Teaching Input 5

- What month are we in now? What year are we in?
- Would you use seconds, minutes or hours to measure:

  The time it takes to walk home?

  The time it takes eat a packet of crisps?

  The time it takes read a book?

  The time you sleep each night?

  The time it takes to travel to London?
- Can you tell me what half past three would be on a digital clock?

PCM 28

Ask the children to complete the clocks by drawing in the hands on the analogue clocks and writing in the numbers on the digital ones.

Shape and Space

This week we will be working on 2D and 3D shapes, recognising and using the four compass directions and describing and finding positions on a grid.

OBJECTIVES

- To use mathematical terms to identify and describe 2D and 3D shapes.
- To make and describe right-angled turns.
- To describe and find a position on a grid.
- To know and use the four compass directions.

LANGUAGE

square, rectangle, hexagon, circle, semicircle, sphere, hemisphere • quadrilaterals, prisms, cube, cuboid, cylinder, cone, triangular prism • horizontal, vertical, diagonal • symmetry, symmetrical • North, South, East, West

RESOURCES

Selection of 2D and 3D shapes, Geostrips, interlocking cubes, Pupils' Book pages 35, 36, 37 and 38, 3 × 3 pinboard, elastic bands, square dotted paper, PCM 29, squared paper.

Teaching Input 1

selection of 2D and 3D shapes, Geostrips

- Could you tell me something about quadrilaterals? Are there any rules? Is there anything else?

Give each child a 2D shape and ask them to describe its features. Do the rest of the group think the description is clear and easy to understand? Were all the sides, vertices and angles included? Make sure each child has a turn describing.

Then ask each child to make a quadrilateral using Geostrips.

- Look carefully at them and discuss whether they are all different. Are any the same? Are any similar shapes different only in size?
- We are now going to look at 3D shapes.
- Tell me some facts about a prism. Can you think of any others?

Hold up a cone, a cylinder, a cube, a cuboid, a pyramid, a sphere and a hemisphere and ask the children to name them.

Then give each child a shape, ask them to hide it and to describe it to the group without naming it. For example, if it were a cube, they could say 'It has six faces, eight vertices and twelve edges'. Each child should take a turn.

interlocking cubes, Pupils' Book page 35

Ask the children to complete the building page in the Pupils' Book.

- Can you describe your work? What problems did you encounter? Is there a pattern? Is there a formula? Could you make a building with ten floors? How many cubes would be needed?

3 × 3 pinboard, elastic bands, square dotted paper

Tell the children they are going to work in pairs to investigate quadrilaterals.

Ask them to make as many quadrilaterals as they can, recording on the square dotted paper.

- How many different quadrilaterals did you discover? Do you think you have them all?
- Has anyone anything different? Did any of you find it more difficult than you expected?

Teaching Input 2

- What do we mean by symmetry?
- What do we mean by lines of symmetry?
- Can you tell me what we mean by the number of lines of symmetry?
- Can you think of a capital letter that has a line of symmetry? *Ask each child in turn.*

- What are compass directions? Can you give me the four compass directions? *Draw them on a sheet of paper and explain.*

- Can you explain horizontal, vertical and diagonal?

 PCM 29

Ask the children to see how many routes they can find by following the direction instructions.

- Can you explain what you have been doing? Can you tell me one of your routes? *For example, S, W, W, W, S, S. Are there any others?*

Teaching Input 3

 selection of 2D shapes, interlocking cubes

- How many sides and how many vertices does a triangle have?

- How many sides and how many vertices does a hexagon have?

- How many sides and how many vertices does a hemisphere have?

- How many sides and how many vertices does a circle have?

- How many sides and how many vertices does a square have?

- How many sides and how many vertices does a rectangle have?

Now give the children a handful of interlocking cubes and ask them to make a shape plus its mirror image.

- Are they all right? Is your model symmetrical?

- Could you draw your model on squared paper?

- What do you discover?

- What do we mean by an angle?

- Can you tell me what we mean by a right angle?

- If you turn round to face the opposite direction, how many right angles have you turned through?

- How can we sort the shapes into three sets? Draw the following on the board

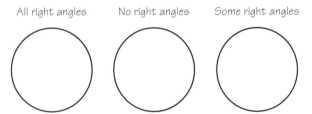

All right angles · · · No right angles · · · Some right angles

- Can you tell me the four compass directions?

 Pupils' Book pages 36 and 37, squared paper

Ask the children to complete the 'Snake Island' exercise in the Pupils' Book by using the map to answer the questions.

- Now use the squared paper to draw your own islands. Then write out five questions for your friends to answer.

 Pupils' Book page 38

Ask the children to do the '3D shape' work described in the Pupils' Book. Remind them that to succeed, they will need to work carefully and systematically.

Reasoning

This week we will be solving mathematical problems and puzzles, asking questions and explaining the work.

Teaching Input 1

- What are the odd numbers between 14 and 20? 21 and 35? 96 and 104?

Repeat several times

- Can you give me a rule about odd numbers? Is there another rule? *For example, two even numbers plus an odd number makes an odd number; one odd plus one even number makes an odd number; an odd number is always one more or one less than an even number.*
- Can you give me some multiples of 10?
- Can you give me some multiples of 5?
- Can you give me some multiples of 2?
- What is 2×5? 5×2? 2×10? 10×2?
- Double 20 is 40. Half of 40 is 20. Now give me some examples of ways to make 40.

Tell the children they may use the numbers 2, 3, 4 and 5 and $+$, $-$, $\times$, $\div$ and $=$ to make as many numbers as they can. They may use the numbers and the signs as often as you decide.

- Can you make every number up to 40?
- How many different answers can you make between 40 and 200?

- Have you found all the numbers? Which numbers do you not have? Have some numbers been made in several ways? Can you see any patterns?

Teaching Input 2

- If all squares have four sides, what rules can you give me for other shapes such as rectangles, hexagons, circles, triangles and quadrilaterals?
- What can you tell me about the two times-table? Is there anything else?
- What can you tell me about the ten times-table? Anything else?
- What can you tell me about the five times-table?
- Work out $25 + 19$, $33 + 11$, $63 + 9$, $23 + 18$ and $45 + 45$. How did you solve them?
- What is $100 \div 2$? $50 \div 2$? $40 \div 2$? And $36 \div 2$? How did you work them out?
- Tell me the answers to 2×10, 2×15, 2×20 and 2×500.
- Work out $60 - 29$, $72 - 19$ and $80 - 19$.
- How about $867 - 100$? $999 - 100$? And $410 - 100$?

scrap paper

Draw a blank 3×3 grid on the board and ask the children to copy it into their books. Tell them they must fill in the numbers 1 to 9 so that each horizontal, vertical and diagonal line of three numbers adds up to 15 (a magic square). If they struggle with this, you may like to give them one or more of the numbers to start them off. One possible solution is as follows:

4	3	8
9	5	1
2	7	6

- Did you find this work difficult? Could you find a different total using the same numbers? Using different numbers?

Teaching Input 3

- What is double 50? Double 500? Double 5000?

- Tell me double 30, double 300 and double 3000.

- In turn, give me a similar sum showing a pattern.

- Tell me the even numbers between 18 and 40, 70 and 90, 101 and 110.

- What is half of 1000? Of 500? Of 200? Of 80?

- Can you tell me 5 × 2? 5 × 3? 5 × 4? 5 × 5? 5 × 10?

- There are three numbers less than 10 which divide exactly by 3. What are they?

- Tell me two numbers which add up to 37, 400, 256, 132, 97 and 550. Are there alternative solutions?

- Tell me three numbers which add up to 300, 500, 175, 250 and 100.

- If you divide 9 by 4, what is the remainder?

- If you divide 12 by 4, what is the answer?

- If you divide 20 by 5, what is the answer?

- If you divide 22 by 5, what is the answer?

Repeat several times.

PCM 30

Ask the children to complete the 'number maze' exercise on the PCM.

- How many throws did it take you to get out?

- Are some numbers easier to make than others? Why do you think that is?

matchsticks or lolly sticks

Give the children seven sticks and ask them to make three triangles. How many sticks would you need to make four, five, six, seven, eight, nine and ten triangles?

The seven sticks made up three triangles. Can you get fewer triangles by moving only two sticks? Explain how you did it.

Counting and Properties of Number, Reasoning about Numbers

This week we are going to solve mathematical problems, explain reasoning and describe and extend number sequences.

OBJECTIVES

- To recognise and extend number sequences and patterns.
- To complete sequences with 'missing' numbers.
- To count on or back in steps of various sizes from any 3-digit number.
- To recognise 2- and 3-digit multiples of 2, 5 and 10.

LANGUAGE

sequence, pattern • rule, formula • question

RESOURCES

Pupils' Book page 39, PCM 31.

Teaching Input 1

- Count on in tens from 0 to 120, and back.
- Count on in tens from 0 to 70, and back.
- Now count on in hundreds from 250 to 1050.
- How many tens are there between 20 and 60? Between 30 and 80? Between 40 and 100?
- Start at 330 and count back in tens to 250.
- Start at 670 and count back in tens to 600.
- Can you tell me what an odd number is? What are some of the rules for odd numbers?
- Can you give me some odd numbers between 270 and 290, 367 and 431?

 Ask the children to work in pairs, noting their working in their books.

Ask each child to pick two numbers between 0 and 50 and to write them at the top of the page with the two numbers their partner chose. (Suggest that they do not pick all high numbers, as this is more difficult.) Ask them to use the four numbers and any mathematical operation to try to make 100.

- Can you make 100 in different ways? *For example, if the numbers were 2, 10, 50 and 30, they might write $2 \times 50 = 100$, $50 + 50 = 100$, $10 \times 2 + 50 + 30$, and so on.*
- What other totals can you make with your numbers?
- Are some totals impossible to make? Why?

Teaching Input 2

- Describe and continue this pattern: 64, 67, 70 …
- And this one: 61, 68, 75 …
- What about: 1000, 900, 800, 700 …?
- Tell me all the multiples of 10 up to 100.
- What are all the multiples of 5 up to 100?
- Can you tell me all the multiples of 2 up to 100?
- Which is the odd one out: 15, 25, 35, 46, 55?
- Count on in hundreds from 200 to 1000, and back.
- Count on in fifties to 600, and back.

 Give the children some number sequences to complete in their books. For example:

136, 130, 124 …

2, 4, 6, 8 …

6, 9, 12 …

100, 90, 81, 73 …

2, 4, 7, 11 …

136, 133, 130 …

- Can you continue the sequences and describe the pattern? When you have finished, try making up your own sequences. You may use the maths operations $+$, $-$, $\times$ and $\div$.

Teaching Input 3

- Count on in fives from 15 to 50, and back.
- Count on in fives from 545 to 600, and back.
- Count 10 back from 820.
- Can you count 8 back from 36? 8 back from 45? 8 back from 100?

Repeat several times.

- Is 767 an odd number? Is 954 an odd number? Is 977 odd? Is 1001 odd? Is 1011 odd?
- How do you know for sure? What do you look at?
- Tell me two numbers which add up to 80, to 74, to 104 and to 200. Are there any other combinations?

Repeat several times.

Pupils' Book page 39

Ask the children to complete the 'Wheels' exercise. Point out the example, explaining the operation in the centre. If the work is finished quickly, they can draw their own blank wheels and put their own numbers and operations in them.

- What can you tell me about your work? Did you check it? What was the hardest part?

Teaching Input 4

- If $2 \times 5 = 5 \times 2$, can you give me other similar examples? *Each child should be given the opportunity to contribute.*
- How many do you add to 75 to make 90?

- How many do you add to 88 to make 95?
- How many do you add to 101 to make 107?
- What is double 20? Double 30? Double 40? Double 100? Double 25? Double 35? Double 45? Double 33? Double 44 and double 55?
- Continue the pattern: $5 + 7\quad = 12$
  $$50 + 70 = 120$$
- Can each of you give a similar example?

Tell the children they can use the numbers 2, 3 and 5, and the operators $+$, $-$, $\times$, $\div$ and $=$.

- Can you make every number between 1 and 50 (or 1 and 100, as appropriate)?
- Show how you can make each number.
- Do you have a pattern, a rule or a formula?

Teaching Input 5

- Add $83 + 12$. How did you work it out?
- What is $830 + 120$?

Repeat several times.

- Add $15 + 15 + 20$.
- How about $25 + 25 + 25 + 25$? $50 + 50$? $500 + 500$? $5000 + 5000$?
- Tell me two numbers which make 70.
- Tell me two 2-digit numbers which make 70. Are there any more?

Repeat several times.

- What is $29 + 31$? $290 + 310$?

Repeat several times.

PCM 31

Ask the children to cut out the jigsaw and reassemble the pieces as a spiral 100-square.

Understanding × and ÷, and Mental Calculation Strategies

This week we are working on multiplication (×) and division (÷), extending ideas and using number facts.

OBJECTIVES

- To recognise that division is the inverse of multiplication and halving is the inverse of doubling.
- To find remainders after simple division.
- To check results with an equivalent calculation.

LANGUAGE

double, halve, multiply, divide • operation, consecutive, target number • multiples, half, quarter

RESOURCES

Pupils' Book pages 40 and 41, dominoes, scrap paper, scissors, pencils, PCM 32.

Teaching Input 1

- What is double 10? Double 20? Double 0? Double 40? Double 100? Double 500? And double 250?
- What is double 25? Double 35? Double 45? Double 55?
- Tell me half of 1000. Half of 500. Half of 300. Of 200. Of 50. Of 30. Of 20 and of 10.
- Can you give me any multiples of 2?
- Can you give me some multiples of 5?
- Tell me some multiples of 10.
- What is 2 × 9? And 9 × 2? Give me a similar pair of sums.

Pupils' Book page 40

Ask the children to complete the 'Number gates' exercise in the Pupils' Book. They should choose one of the number gates at the top of the page and put a set of three ball numbers through that operation. For example, they might choose ×10 for the first set, and so 12 becomes 120, 19 becomes 190 and 15 becomes 150.

Teaching Input 2

- What is 4 × 5? 5 × 4? 6 × 2? 2 × 6? 2 × 12? 12 × 2?

- Can you give me a rule about multiplication?
- What is 20 ÷ 2? And 20 ÷ 10? And 20 ÷ 5?
- Can you give me another sum, dividing 20 by different numbers?
- What happens when you divide 20 by 6? What do you call the number left over? It is the remainder. The remainder is important and it should always be stated.
- Can you tell me what 20 divided by 5 is? How can you check if you are correct?
- How many tens are there in 70? 80? 100?
- How many fives are there in 20? 40? 50?
- How many twos are there in 20? 18? 12?

Pupils' Book page 41, dominoes

Tell the children they are going to play a game for two players using dominoes.

The children should follow the instructions in the Pupils' Book.

The winner is the one with most points at the end of the game.

Teaching Input 3

- Which two numbers can I multiply together to make 20? 30? 48? 24? And 50? Is there more than one way?

Repeat with other numbers.

- The number 46 can be made by 5 × 9 + 1 = 46. How might you make 47? 17? And 11?

Repeat several times.

- What would quarter of 100 be? And of 40? How did you work it out?
- Can you give me half of 40 and half of 20?

Repeat several times.

scrap paper, scissors

Adult supervision recommended

Tell the children they are going to play 'Targets', a game for two players.

Write the following numbers on the board:

5 5 6 6 7 7 8 8 9 9
10 10 12 12 20 20

Ask each pair to copy the numbers onto some scrap paper and to cut them out. They then place the numbers face down on the table.

Before starting the game, you need to tell them a 'target' number.

Tell the players they may use ×, ÷, =, 2, 3 and 5 (use other numbers, if more appropriate).

Each child chooses a number at random from the table and decides whether to multiply *or* divide by 2, 3 or 5, recording in their books.

As they play, each player should keep a running total by adding their first total to their second and so on.

At the end of eight turns, the person to reach the target or who is closer to it wins.

If the target number is exceeded, however, that player is out and the other wins. Remind the children that they must show all their workings.

Note: The children will need supervision until they are confident of the rules.

- Can you describe your game? What have you been doing? Can you tell me how you achieved your total?

Teaching Input 4

Write the following on the board or a large sheet of paper.

$7 \times 5 = 35$, so, $35 \div 5 = 7$
$5 \times 7 = 35$, so, $35 \div 7 = 5$

- Now you are going to write down some similar statements. Start with 6×4.

Note: Encourage each child in the group to write similar statements as this way of thinking does help.

Play 'Consecutive numbers'.

Write the following numbers on the board:

4   7   6   8   5

- Multiply the numbers which are next to each other, for example, 4×7 and 8×5. Now add together all the answers, recording your work.
- If you rearrange the numbers what happens?
- How many different totals can you make?
- Now try it again using a different set of five muddled-up consecutive numbers.

- Can you tell me what you discovered? What were your totals? Did anyone manage anything different? How did you work them out?

Teaching Input 5

- What rules do we know about multiples of 10, 5 and 2? Are there any others?
- What is 7×10? 70×10? 7×100? And 5×10?
- What is $800 \div 10$? $800 \div 100$? $400 \div 10$? And $400 \div 100$?
- How many hundreds are there in 1000?
- What is 20×3? 20×4? 20×5?
- What is one third of 6? 9? 12? 15? 18?
- Which number do I multiply by 15 to make 30? And 60?

PCM 32

Ask the children to complete the millipedes calculation sequences on the PCM.

- Did you check your answers? How did you do that? Did you notice anything about your work?

Money and Real Life Problems, Making Decisions and Checking Results

This week we are going to work mainly on problems connected with money. We will be making decisions and checking results.

OBJECTIVES

• To solve more complex real life problems using appropriate operations, check results and explain how the problem was solved.

LANGUAGE

double, half, vertical, horizontal, diagonal • combinations • share

RESOURCES

Dice, counters, pencils, paper, Pupils' Book page 42, PCMs 33 and 34.

Teaching Input 1

• What is 2×5? What is 2×6? What is 2×7? How could you check you have the correct answer? What do you notice?

Repeat with similar patterns.

• What is $46 + 37$? How did you work it out? Is there another way?

• What about 2×12? How did you calculate it? Is there another way?

• If my chips cost £1.10 and my drink cost 90p, how much did I spend altogether?

• If I think of a number and add 10, my answer is 31. What was my number?

• If I think of a number, double it and add 2, my answer is 20. What was my number?

Repeat each activity several times.

dice, counters, pencils, paper

Draw this grid on the board and ask the children to copy it on their paper.

1	2	3	4	5	6
7	8	9	10	11	12
13	14	15	16	17	18
19	20	21	22	23	24
25	26	27	28	29	30
31	32	33	34	35	36

Tell them they are going to play a game in groups of up to three, and that each player should take four counters. Using three dice, they take turns to throw them and use those three numbers and the operations $+$, $-$, $\times$ and $\div$ to try to make one of the numbers on the grid. For example, if they throw 6, 6 and 3, they can make 33 ($6 \times 6 - 3$). If they manage to make one of the numbers, they should put a counter on that number. The first player to make four in a row, vertically, horizontally or diagonally, wins the game.

• Which part of the game was most difficult? Were some numbers easier to make? Were there any numbers you could not make?

Teaching Input 2

• If a dog has four legs, how many legs will five dogs have? How many will ten dogs have?

Repeat several times.

• If I have 12 toffees, six lemon sherbets and five jelly babies, how many sweets have I altogether? If I share them among six children, how many sweets will each one get? Will there be any left over? If everyone was given one more, how many more sweets would I need?

• How many pennies are there in £4.68? In £5.45? In £7.02?

Repeat several times.

• How many pounds and pennies are there in 395p? In 662p? In 121p?

• If a comic costs 15p, how much do I need for two comics? For five comics? For eight comics and for ten comics?

Tell the children to work in their books to investigate different ways to make the following amounts, recording in their books.

- What coins could you use to pay £2.25?
- What coins could you use to pay £1.95?
- What coins could you use to pay £1.92?
- What coins could you use to pay £3.70?

 • What combinations for each of those amounts did you find? Did anyone write down anything different?

Teaching Input 3

 • I have 70p in three coins. What are they?

- I have 90p in three coins. What are they?
- I have £1 in four coins. What are they?
- I have £2 in four coins. What are they?
- How many pounds are there in 612p? In 733p? In 919? In 970p? And in 141p?
- How many pennies are there in £10? And in £9.59?
- I am saving £1.50 each week. How much do I save in five weeks? In ten weeks?
- I want to buy a coat which costs £55. If I get £35 per week, how many weeks will I have to wait until I can buy the coat?

 Pupils' Book page 42

Ask the children to calculate the amounts each stall could take by adding up the prices carefully.

 • How did you work out the totals? What was the highest total? The lowest total?

Teaching Input 4

 • How many 50p pieces make £1? £2? £3.50 and £10?

Repeat several times.

- How many 20p pieces make £1? £2? And £5?
- How many 10p pieces make £1? And £3?

Repeat several times.

- If you used five coins to pay 30p, what would they be? What if you were paying 74p? And £1?

- If one apple costs 12p, how much would three apples cost? Five apples?

 pencils, paper, PCMs 33 and 34

Ask the children to work in pairs, using the paper and pencils for recording.

Give each pair a copy of PCMs 33 and 34. Tell them to decide who will be A and who will be B and to take the appropriate PCMs. They should add together the amounts at the corners of each hexagon and write the total in the centre. Then they can match them to the segments on their millipede.

 • Did you find this difficult? If so, which part? How did you work out the amounts? Did everyone get the same results?

Teaching Input 5

 • If two apples cost 45p each, how much change do I get from £1?

- If one orange costs 55p, how much would six cost? How much would four cost?
- Would you rather get 60p each week as pocket money, or £3 every four weeks?
- If eight bars of chocolate cost 72p, how much would one cost?

 Ask the children to record the answers to these problems in their books.

- If one drink costs 70p, what will two drinks cost?
- If I gave you £5 to pay for your drinks, how much change would you get?
- Your pocket money is 80p per day. How much do you get in one week? If you gave £1 a week to charity, how much would you have left?
- You go shopping for your family with a £5 note and you spend £3.25. How much change will you have? Could you afford to buy a £1.90 comic with the change? How much more do you need?
- You go to the cinema and your ticket costs £2.20. You have £2.80 left, so how much did you start with?
- Two books cost £3 each, a newspaper 70p and a comic £1.55. What was my total bill? What coins could I pay it with?

Fractions

This week we are going to work on fractions, recognising them as part of a whole and comparing familiar fractions.

OBJECTIVES

- To find simple fractions of whole numbers up to 20.
- To recognise patterns in fractions of odd and even numbers.
- To find equivalents of non-unit fractions.
- To begin to use fractions in real life problems.

LANGUAGE

fraction • half, quarter, three quarters, one whole, one fifth, one sixth, one eighth, one tenth • equally • rule • remainder, dividing, whole number, halfway

RESOURCES

Counters, Pupils' Book page 43, interlocking cubes, large sheets of paper, PCM 35.

Teaching Input 1

- What do we mean by a fraction?
- What fractions do you know?
- How many halves are there in a whole?
- How many sixths are there in a half?
- How many quarters are there in a whole?
- Can you explain what we mean by $\frac{1}{4}$, $\frac{3}{4}$, $\frac{1}{3}$, and $\frac{2}{3}$?
- If you have a cake and cut it into quarters, how many quarters would you get?

Repeat with fifths, tenths, sixths, and so on.

Ask the children to draw some squares in their books. They should work with a partner to divide each square up into halves and decorate one half. For example:

Remind them to make their designs as varied and interesting as possible.

As an extension, they might draw rectangles or hexagons and colour half of the shape.

- Can you tell me about your halves? Has anyone made an interesting design?

Teaching Input 2

counters

- What is half of 4? Half of 6? Of 8? Of 10? Of 12? Of 20?
- What would half of 5 be? Are you sure?
- What is half of 7? Of 9? Of 11?
- What can you tell me about halving odd numbers?
- What can you tell me about halving even numbers?

Give the children a handful of counters and ask them to work in pairs to check the rule about even and odd numbers. That is, an odd number always has 1 left over to be shared when divided by 2 which is an extra half. For example, $15 = 7\frac{1}{2} + 7\frac{1}{2} = 14 + \frac{1}{2} + \frac{1}{2} = 15$.

Repeat this until they are confident.

counters

Ask the children to copy the following table in their books.

No. of counters	$\frac{1}{2}$	$\frac{1}{4}$	$\frac{3}{4}$	$\frac{1}{3}$	$\frac{2}{3}$	$\frac{1}{6}$	$\frac{1}{8}$	$\frac{1}{10}$	$\frac{1}{12}$	$\frac{1}{5}$			

Tell them that they are going to work on the numbers 6, 8, 10, 12, 15, 16, 18 and 20.

Select a number, take that number of counters and work out each fraction of the number in the table. They do not need to fill in each square every time – only if the number is suitable.

- Are some numbers easier to work with than others? Did you manage to get one fifth of any number? Did you manage to get one eighth of any number? Did you manage to get one sixth of any number?

Teaching Input 3

- What is another way to write $\frac{2}{4}, \frac{3}{6}, \frac{4}{8}, \frac{5}{10}, \frac{10}{10}, \frac{5}{5}$ and $\frac{4}{4}$?

- Which number is halfway between 5 and 6?

- Which number is halfway between 6 and 7? Between 9 and 10? Between 15 and 16?

- If I have two quarters and one half, how much have I altogether?

- What about $\frac{3}{4}$ and $\frac{1}{4}$?

- What is $\frac{5}{10} + \frac{5}{10}$? $\frac{4}{8} + \frac{4}{8}$?

Pupils' Book page 43

Ask the children to complete the 'Domino fractions' exercise in the Pupils' Book, filling in their grids with the answers.

Teaching Input 4

interlocking cubes

- What is half of 2? Of 4? Of 6? Of 8? Of 10? Of 50? *Make sure they are all even numbers.*

- What is quarter of 4? Of 8? Of 12? Of 16? Of 20?

Hand out the interlocking cubes and ask the children to show:

1. One fifth of 5 (say 1 red and 4 black cubes), one fifth of 10, one fifth of 15 and one fifth of 20.

2. One sixth of 6, one sixth of 12, one sixth of 18 and one sixth of 20.

3. One tenth of 10, one tenth of 20, one tenth of 30, one tenth of 40 and one tenth of 50.

large sheets of paper, PCM 35

Ask the children to draw 0 to 10 number lines on large sheets of paper, using at least a 2 centimetre width per number. Then ask them to fill in halves and quarters on it.

When they have completed the task, ask them to complete the PCM. Remind them to be careful and only use one colour.

- Can you use your number line and count forwards and back in steps of one quarter, one half, three quarters, one whole? Now each of you, in turn, ask the group a question about the line.

- How did you work out one quarter of the pattern?

Teaching Input 5

- What is half of 20p? Of 50p? Of 100p? Repeat several times.

- What is quarter of 20p? What about quarter of £1?

- How many 20p pieces make £1?

- How many quarters are there in one whole?

- How many lots of 25p are there in £1?

- If I have 20 sweets to share equally with a friend, how many sweets would I get?

- Which is the biggest: $\frac{1}{2}, \frac{4}{5}$ or $\frac{3}{4}$? Put them in order.

- Put $\frac{7}{8}, \frac{3}{8}, \frac{5}{8}$ and $\frac{4}{8}$ in order, smallest first.

- Put $\frac{6}{10}, \frac{2}{10}, \frac{5}{10}$ and $\frac{8}{10}$ in order, smallest first.

- If you add $\frac{1}{4} + \frac{1}{4}$ together, what do you get? What about $\frac{1}{2} + \frac{1}{2}$? What about $\frac{1}{4} + \frac{1}{4}$?

- Write the answers to these questions as fractions:

1. If one cake is shared equally between four people, how much does each get?

2. If one cake is shared equally between ten people, how much does each get?

3. If one cake is shared equally between five people, how much does each get?

- How did you get on with your work? What can you tell me about fractions? Can you tell me a fraction, such as half, and ways of writing it?

Understanding + and −, Paper and Pencil Procedures and Problems, including Time

This week we will be consolidating work on +, −, mental calculation strategies and time, including problems.

OBJECTIVES

- To use number patterns, strategies and rapid recall of number facts.
- To perform mental calculations in an efficient manner.
- To read and interpret timetables.
- To construct a timeline and to be aware of the passage of time.

LANGUAGE

methods of calculation • time line, date of birth, digital/analogue clocks, timetable

RESOURCES

Paper, pencils, PCMs 36 and 37, Pupils' Book pages 44 and 45.

Teaching Input 1

- Answer the following questions as quickly as you can.
- What is 89 + 10, 96 + 11, 27 + 9, 51 + 9, 70 + 9, 84 + 6 and 72 + 8?
- What is 54 + 11, 63 + 6, 26 + 11 and 26 + 9?
- Tell me two numbers which make 30.
- Tell me three numbers which total 20.
- What is 20 − 10, 35 − 11, 16 − 9, 99 − 9 and 999 − 990?
- What is 10 less than 990?
- What is 100 less than 990?
- Give me two numbers with a difference of 5.

Repeat several times.

Ask the children to use any 2-digit numbers, + and − to make the following numbers: 100, 95, 90, 64 and 72. They may use + and − several times, if they wish, but they should always have a combination.

- Can you tell me how you made that? What happens if you reverse the numbers or operators?

Teaching Input 2

paper, pencils

- Add 38 + 12. How did you work it out? For example, 30 + 10 = 40, 8 + 2 = 10 and 40 + 10 = 50. Could you have used a different method? What could it be?
- Repeat with 46 + 14, 59 + 13 and 151 + 29. How did you do them?
- Can you tell me what 501 − 495 is? What method did you use?
- What about 6670 − 666?

Repeat several times.

- What is 46 + 45? What is 36 + 34? And 80 + 90? How did you work them out? Did you double up first?

Repeat several times.

PCM 36

Ask the children to complete the hexagons by adding the numbers in the corners and writing the total in the centre. If there is time, the children might make up and fill in their own hexagons.

- What can you tell me about your work?
- What did you discover? Did you work in your head or did you write it down and work on paper? What method of calculating did you use? Did you use near doubles? Did you use another method?

Teaching Input 3

Work through these number patterns. It can help to write them on the board.

Continue the pattern:

$8 + 4 \quad = 12$
$80 + 40 \ =$
$14 + 2 \quad = 16$
$140 + 20 =$

Each child should be asked, in turn, to give a pattern and write it on the board. Explain that if you can see patterns in numbers, it makes calculations and estimations much easier.

Ask the children to choose any four numbers from the following list:

28   60   49   97   104   19   55

They may use $+$, $−$ and $=$ with the numbers as many times as they like to make as many totals as possible.

- Which numbers did you choose?
- Why did you choose those numbers?
- Tell me what you did.
- Did you have difficulties?
- Would it have helped if you had put the numbers in a different order?
- Would it have changed the total?
- What was the largest total you made? The smallest total?

Teaching Input 4

- Answer the following questions as quickly as you can: $351 + 100$, $666 + 100$, $969 + 100$, $905 − 100$ and $884 − 100$.

Repeat several times.

- What is $904 − 898$? How did you work it out? Did you count on?
- What is $678 − 671$?

Repeat this activity.

- Now, as you explain the following, write it on the board so all the children can see it.
- What is $87 + 56$? This could be done as $80 + 50 = 130$ and $7 + 6 = 13$. Therefore, $87 + 56 = 130 + 13 = 143$. It might also be done as $85 + 50 = 135 + 8 = 143$.
- Now how about $145 + 330$?

PCM 37

Give the children PCM 37 and explain to them what a time line is.

Suggest they fill each segment with things which are important to them, for instance, their family and friends. They may wish to put in the year they were born, their brother or sister's birthday, and so on. Remind them to think carefully and try to make their timeline interesting. They might like to include, for example, sporting events, school trips or holidays.

Teaching Input 5

- How many seconds are there are in one minute?
- How many minutes are there in an hour?
- How many hours are there in one day?
- How many weeks are there in a year?
- How many weeks are there in two years?
- When is your birthday? What is your date of birth? *Ask each child in the group.*
- If it is 25 minutes to 9, what would show on a digital clock? What about 25 minutes past 9?
- If it is 4:45 on a digital clock, what would show on an analogue one? What about 4:15?
- What is another way of saying 4:30? 4:10? 4:05 and 4:50?

Repeat several times.

Pupils' Book pages 44 and 45, analogue clock

Ask the children to use the timetable to answer the questions in the Pupils' Book. They may need to use the clock.

- What have you noticed? What can you tell me about the timetable? Did you find this work difficult?

Data

This week we will be working on posing questions, collecting data, organising the data, representing and interpreting it and discussing the result.

Teaching Input 1

large sheets of paper, coloured pens

Can you explain what a Venn diagram is?

Note: As you go through the following explanation, draw an example and explain it using the numbers 1 to 20 with one circle representing 'Odd numbers' and the other 'Numbers greater than 7'. Thus the intersection will contain the odd numbers greater than 7.

- Look at this diagram and its two criteria. We have the numbers 1 to 20 here. Can we put them into the appropriate set? *The children should say where the numbers go.*
- What can you tell by looking at the diagram?
- Now can you tell me what a Carroll diagram is?

Repeat the exercise with a Carroll diagram, for example:

	Odd Numbers	Not odd Numbers
More than 7		
Not more than 7		

- What can you tell me by looking at the Carroll diagram?
- Why and when would you make a list?
- Are there other ways of collecting data?

- Ask the children to work in pairs to prove the statement 'Most girls' favourite colour is blue and favourite season is spring'. Can you prove it?

- Decide how you are going to find this out. You can only use the children in the group to test the hypothesis.
- Today you are going to gather the information. We are all going to keep our work and make a display at the end of the week. Make sure you include everyone in the group – both boys and girls!

Teaching Input 2

With the children in pairs, continue the teaching from the previous day.

- Yesterday, you gathered information to find out whether 'Most girls' favourite colour is blue and favourite season is spring'.
- How did you gather the information? Explain what you did.
- Did you make lists – one for boys and one for girls?
- Are they easy to read?

Suggest now that each child should make a list as the example below:

Name	Favourite colour	Favourite season
Lucy	Red	Spring
Naoko	Blue	Summer

- Have you the same number of children on your chart as in the class?
- How do you know that nobody is missing?

large sheets of paper

- Do you remember how to draw a Venn diagram? *Each pair of children will need a Venn diagram, with headings, 'Favourite colour blue' and 'Favourite season spring' drawn on paper to transfer the information from their list.*

- It may help if you cut up one of your lists and place the pieces of paper in the appropriate areas before writing as this will make it easier to decide where to put the names. Save the other list, as it will be needed for tomorrow's work.

- Have you put everyone on the diagram?

Teaching Input 3

- Let us look at the Venn diagram you completed yesterday.

- What can you tell me about it?

- What have you found out?

Do you think it easier to read?

large sheets of paper

Draw the following two Carroll diagrams on the paper.

	Girls	Not girls
Favourite colour blue		
Favourite colour not blue		

	Girls	Not girls
Favourite season spring		
Favourite season not spring		

- Transfer the information you had in your Venn diagram to the Carroll diagrams. Make sure you have included everybody in the class on your diagrams!

Teaching Input 4

- Look at the Carroll diagram. What did you discover?

- Did you find that a lot of children do not say their favourite season is spring?

- Did you find that a lot of children do not say blue is their favourite colour?

- How many girls like blue best?

- How many girls like spring best?

- How many girls are there in the class?

large sheet of paper, computer

Draw out a block graph as below

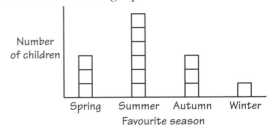

Number of children

Spring   Summer   Autumn   Winter
Favourite season

- Now produce another block graph for favourite colours.

- What can you tell me about it?

- How many children actually choose blue and spring as their favourite colour and season?

- Could we prove the original hypothesis?

Help the children to convert these charts to bar graphs, either by making them or by using a computer with a suitable program.

- Do you think it would make a difference if we collected information from more than one class?

- Would it have made a difference if we collected information from the whole school?

Teaching Input 5

- Each pair should now work out a question to ask the rest of the group.

- Now ask the group some of your questions. Can they answer them?

- Do you think it was a fair survey?

- How could you have changed it?

- Do you think some charts are easier to interpret than others?

- Make a display of all the graphs, charts, diagrams and lists and label them.

- In pairs look at each diagram and write two different statements about each one. *For example, we put all the children's names on the table, their favourite colour and season. It was difficult to see which colour was the most popular.*

They must be able to say what sort of diagram they are describing and something relevant about it.

- Can you describe your work? Has anyone got any different ideas? Which diagram was the easiest to read? Could you make connections between the graphs, charts and diagrams?

Write in the figures or words for the numbers in the snakes.

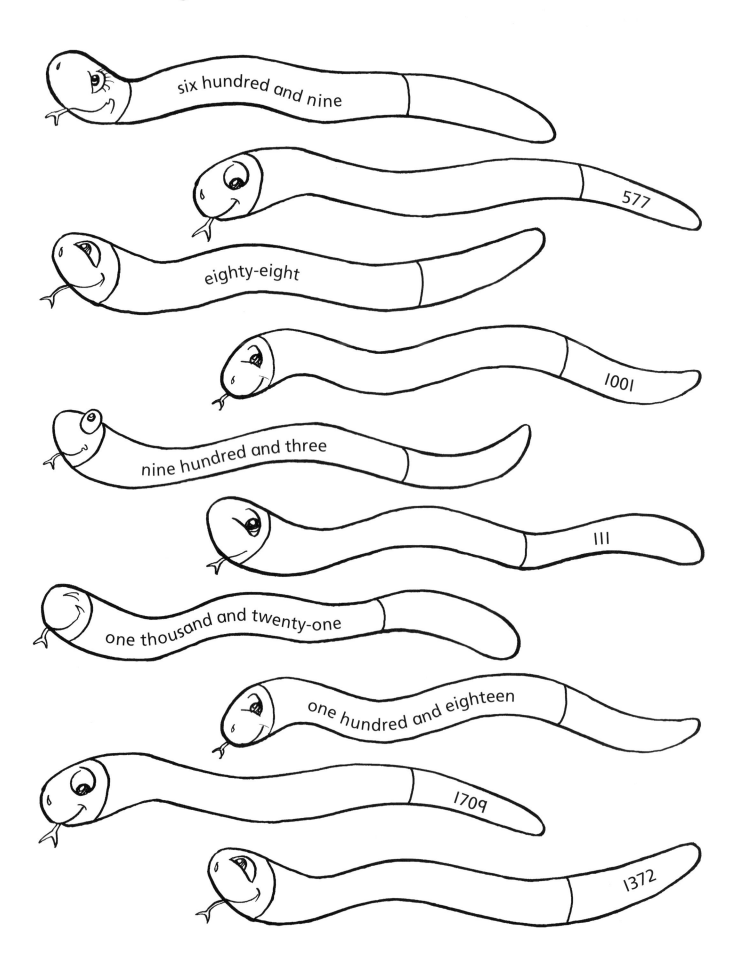

six hundred and nine

577

eighty-eight

1001

nine hundred and three

111

one thousand and twenty-one

one hundred and eighteen

1709

1372

PCM 2

Complete the hexagons. The centre numbers are the totals of the corner numbers. The first one is done for you.

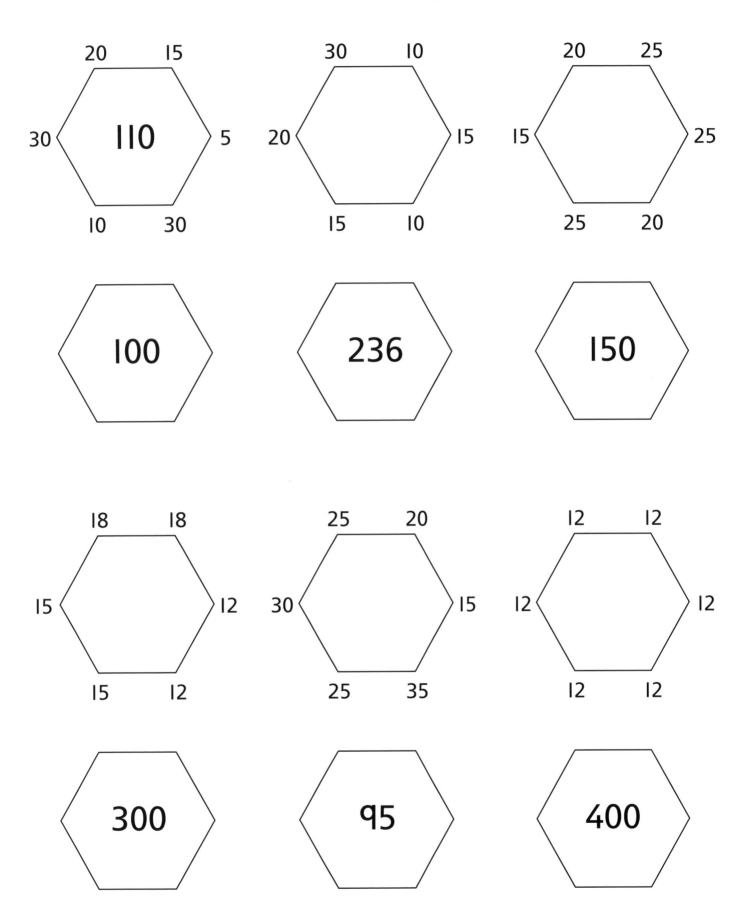

PCM 3

You visit a Burger Bar with a friend.

Fill in the table to show what you could buy.

Write your own amounts in the last three rows.

£1.20 Plain burger	£1.20 Vegetables	45p Drinks
£1.50 Cheese burger	50p Chips	40p Ice cream
£1.75 Triple burger	50p Salad	25p Choc bar
£1.50 Fish burger		

You have	What did you buy?	How much did it cost?	How much change did you recieve?
£2.50			
£3.00			
£4.50			
£5.00			
£10.00			
£6.00			
£20.00			
75p			

PCM 4

Cut out these shapes.

How many shapes can you make by putting them together?

Now try to fit all five shapes inside this one.

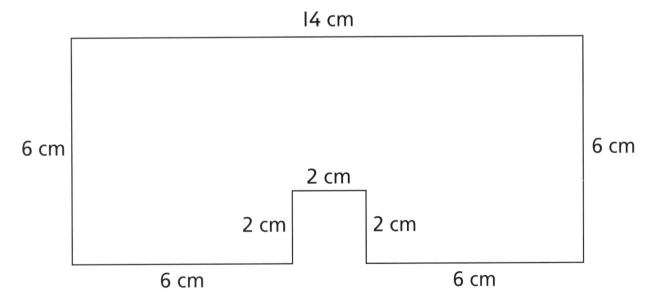

You may use interlocking cubes to make the shapes, but you may not break up the shapes once made

Cut out these shapes.
Can you fit them inside the lorry on PCM 6?

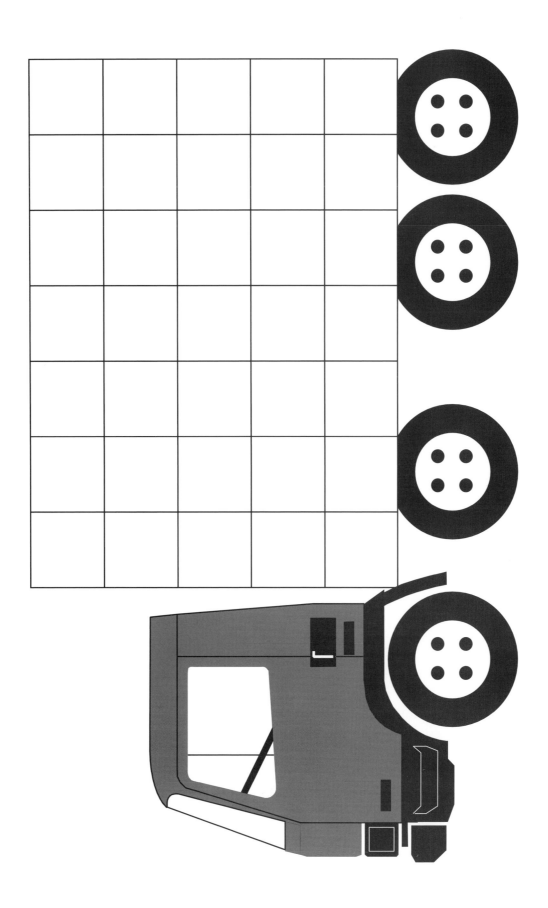

Keep your score on this chart.

Write whether your target was the highest or lowest number.

The winner scores 5 points each game.

	Points A	Points B			Points A	Points B
1 Target: _____ A ☐☐☐ B ☐☐☐				6 Target: _____ A ☐☐☐ B ☐☐☐		
2 Target: _____ A ☐☐☐ B ☐☐☐				7 Target: _____ A ☐☐☐ B ☐☐☐		
3 Target: _____ A ☐☐☐ B ☐☐☐				8 Target: _____ A ☐☐☐ B ☐☐☐		
4 Target: _____ A ☐☐☐ B ☐☐☐				9 Target: _____ A ☐☐☐ B ☐☐☐		
5 Target: _____ A ☐☐☐ B ☐☐☐				10 Target: _____ A ☐☐☐ B ☐☐☐		
Total:				Total:		

100-199 square

100	101	102	103	104	105	106	107	108	109
110	111	112	113	114	115	116	117	118	119
120	121	122	123	124	125	126	127	128	129
130	131	132	133	134	135	136	137	138	139
140	141	142	143	144	145	146	147	148	149
150	151	152	153	154	155	156	157	158	159
160	161	162	163	164	165	166	167	168	169
170	171	172	173	174	175	176	177	178	179
180	181	182	183	184	185	186	187	188	189
190	191	192	193	194	195	196	197	198	199

Make a 'squares snake' from squared paper, using 3 or 4 squares. For example:

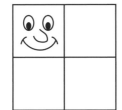 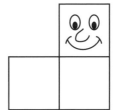

With a friend, take turns to cover squares on the grid.
Add together the covered numbers.
What is the highest total you can make?
What is the smallest?

Multiplication square (I)

1	2	3	4	5	6	7	8	9	10
2	4	6	8	10	12	14	16	18	20
3	6	9	12	15	18	21	24	27	30
4	8	12	16	20	24	28	32	36	40
5	10	15	20	25	30	35	40	45	50
6	12	18	24	30	36	42	48	54	60
7	14	21	28	35	42	49	56	63	70
8	16	24	32	40	48	56	64	72	80
9	18	27	36	45	54	63	72	81	90
10	20	30	40	50	60	70	80	90	100

Draw a line around any 2 × 2 square in the grid, such as:

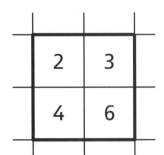

Multiply the numbers in the opposite corners:

2 × 6 = 12   4 × 3 = 12

Repeat this with other 2 × 2 squares, using a different colour each time. Write down the calculations each time.

What do you discover?

Now try a 3 × 3 and 4 × 4 square

What do you find?

How many ways can you find to make the amounts in each hive?

£1.00

50p + 70p − 20p

60p + 10p + 30p

20p + 50p + 30p

£3.00

£1.79

£2.36

£5.00

Now try your own numbers.

Fractions (I)

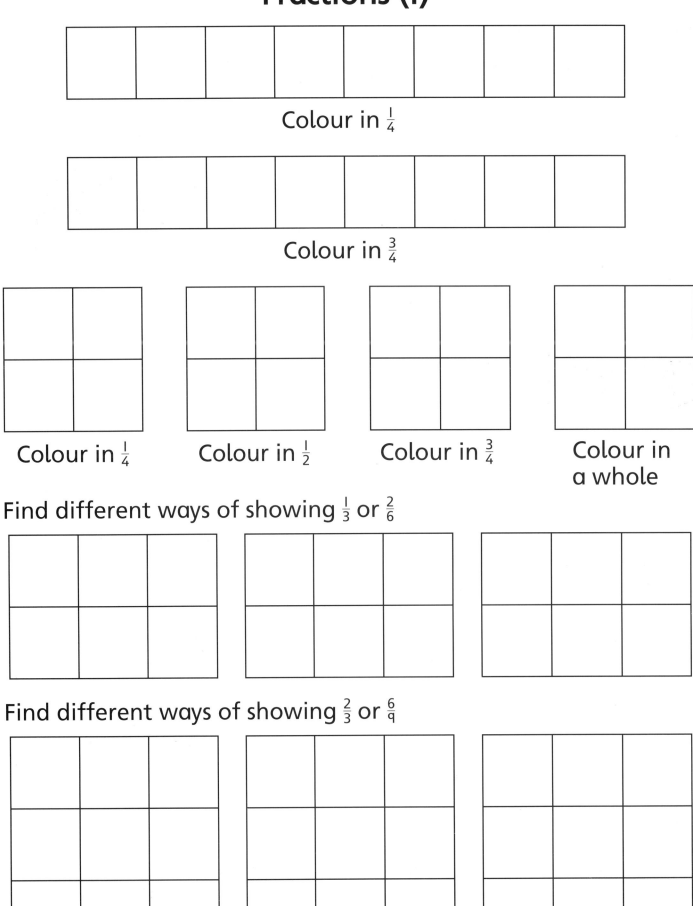

Colour in $\frac{1}{4}$

Colour in $\frac{3}{4}$

Colour in $\frac{1}{4}$ Colour in $\frac{1}{2}$ Colour in $\frac{3}{4}$ Colour in a whole

Find different ways of showing $\frac{1}{3}$ or $\frac{2}{6}$

Find different ways of showing $\frac{2}{3}$ or $\frac{6}{9}$

Fractions (2)

Colour in $\frac{1}{3}$ of this shape

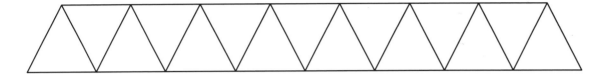

Colour in $\frac{2}{3}$ of this shape

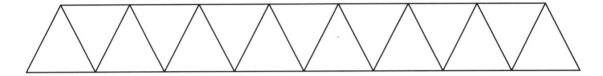

Colour in $\frac{1}{2}$ of this shape

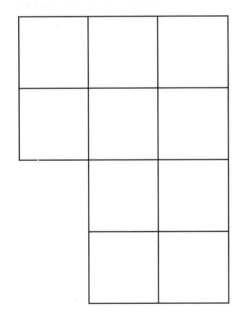

Colour in $\frac{1}{2}$

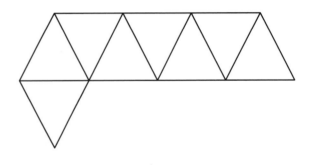

Colour in $\frac{1}{3}$

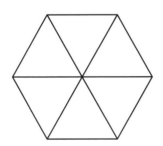

Colour in $\frac{1}{2}$

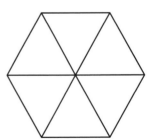

PCM 13

Follow this trail and fill in the squares
Follow the arrow instructions

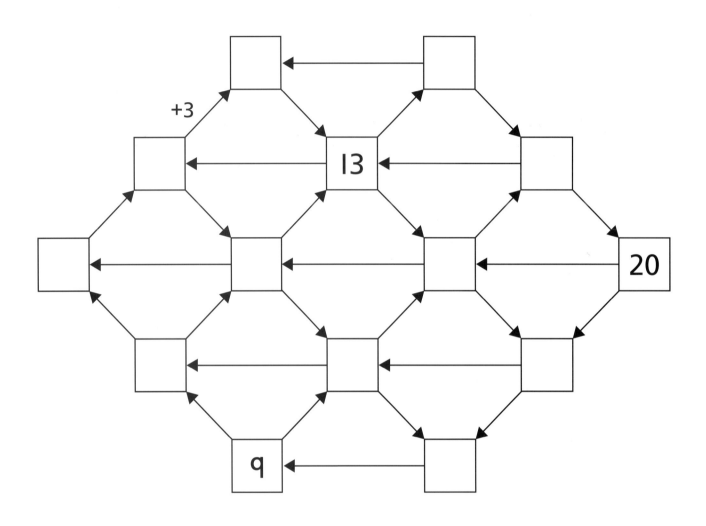

What does ⟵ mean? _____

If (image +3 +2) means 'add 5',

(image) = _____   (image) = _____

101–200 square

101	102	103	104	105	106	107	108	109	110
111	112	113	114	115	116	117	118	119	120
121	122	123	124	125	126	127	128	129	130
131	132	133	134	135	136	137	138	139	140
141	142	143	144	145	146	147	148	149	150
151	152	153	154	155	156	157	158	159	160
161	162	163	164	165	166	167	168	169	170
171	172	173	174	175	176	177	178	179	180
181	182	183	184	185	186	187	188	189	190
191	192	193	194	195	196	197	198	199	200

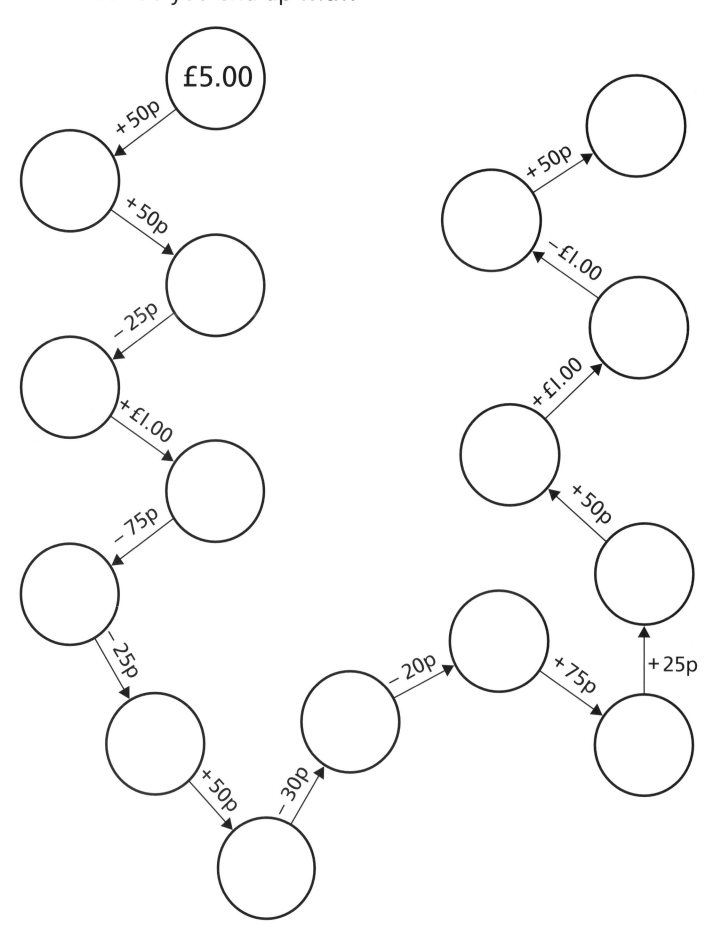

Start at £5 and follow the money trail.
How much do you end up with?

£5.00

+50p

+50p

−25p

+£1.00

−75p

−25p

+50p

−30p

−20p

+75p

+25p

+50p

+50p

−£1.00

+£1.00

PCM 16

> You will need card, scissors, glue, litre jugs, containers, sand/rice/dried peas

Use the net to make a container out of card.

Each square must be 5 cm by 5 cm.

Make an open box.

Fill the box with rice, sand or dried peas.

Pour the contents into a litre jug.

What happens? What do you discover?

The box must be made carefully and measured accurately.

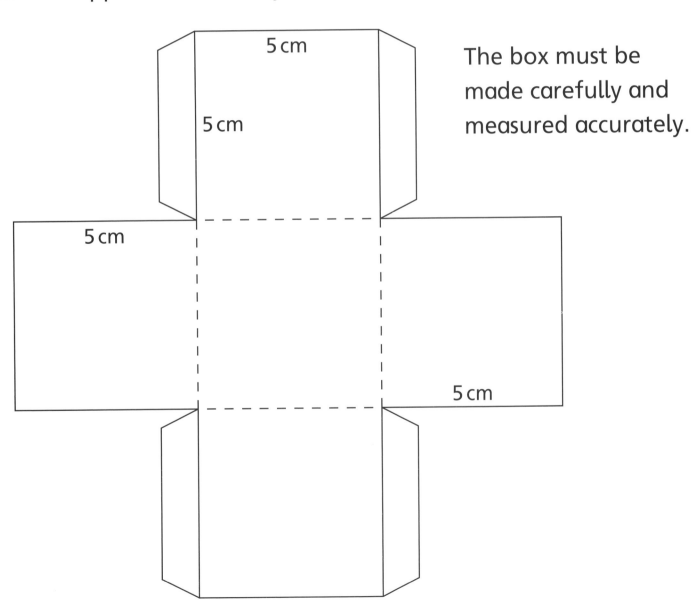

Symmetrical Patterns

Make a patchwork quilt using the squares below.

It must be a symmetrical pattern.

When you have made your quilt you may colour it in.

It must still be symmetrical.

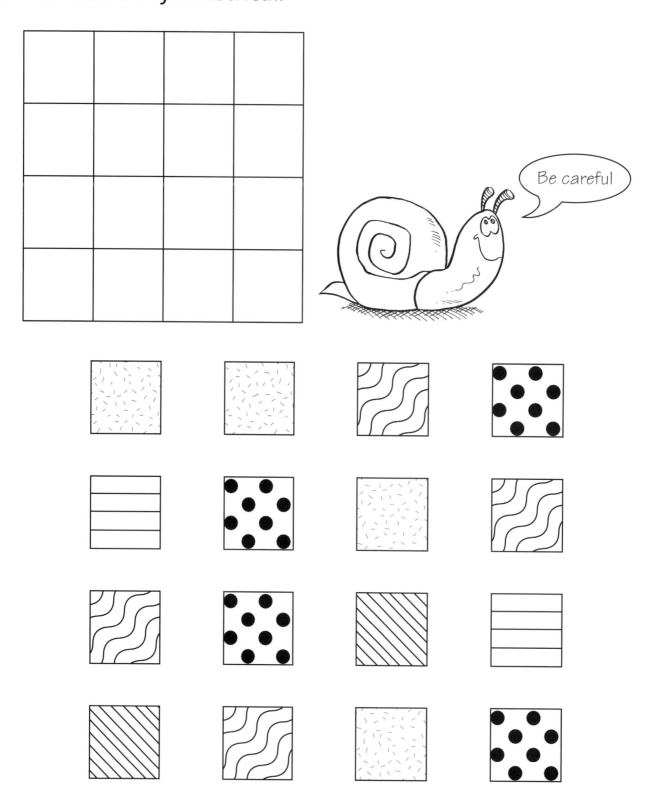

Be careful

121 square

1	2	3	4	⑤	6	7	8	9	⑩	11
12	13	14	15	16	17	18	19	20	21	22
23	24	25	26	27	28	29	30	31	32	33
34	35	36	37	38	39	40	41	42	43	44
45	46	47	48	49	50	51	52	53	54	55
56	57	58	59	60	61	62	63	64	65	66
67	68	69	70	71	72	73	74	75	76	77
78	79	80	81	82	83	84	85	86	87	88
89	90	91	92	93	94	95	96	97	98	99
100	101	102	103	104	105	106	107	108	109	110
111	112	113	114	115	116	117	118	119	120	121

Look at the square. What can you tell me about it?

What patterns can you see?

Choose any number between 1 and 9 and circle it. Now count along the line using that number each time. For example, if you choose 5, jump five and land on 10. Keep counting in fives to see where you land each time, circling that number.

Now start from a different number.

Be careful to count accurately and to circle with a different colour each time you start from a new number.

Which number jumps land on 100? 110? 120?

Repeat using different numbers to jump.

Multiplication square (2)

How many ways can you make 25 by adding numbers from the grid? In each sum you may use each number as many times as it is in the grid. Write down your sums.

Example

$4 + 9 + 12 = 25$.

Now try making 125.

1	2	3	4	5	6	7	8	9	10
2	4	6	8	10	12	14	16	18	20
3	6	9	12	15	18	21	24	27	30
4	8	12	16	20	24	28	32	36	40
5	10	15	20	25	30	35	40	45	50
6	12	18	24	30	36	42	48	54	60
7	14	21	28	35	42	49	56	63	70
8	16	24	32	40	48	56	64	72	80
9	18	27	36	45	54	63	72	81	90
10	20	30	40	50	60	70	80	90	100

Arrows

Choose your starting numbers and then fill in the squares.

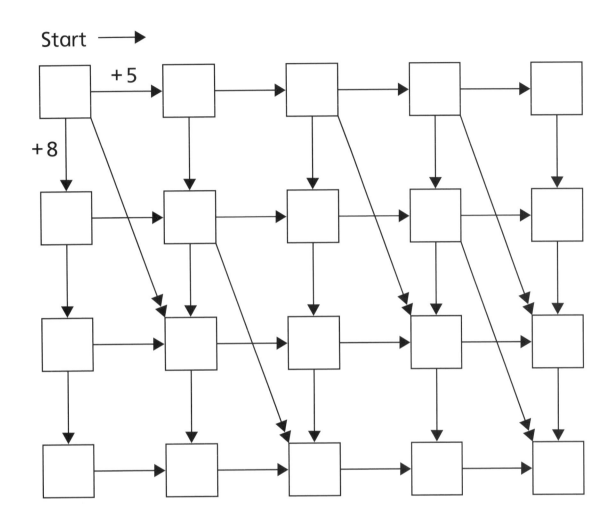

What do ↓ arrows mean?

Can you try with a different starting number?

Can you try with different values for ⟶ and ↓ ?

What did you notice?

Write in numbers so the see-saws balance.

Example

4 + 6   7 + 3

354 − 100   70 + 70

125 + 125   20 x 2

100 ÷ 10   100 ÷ 2

50 + 50 + 50   182 + 26

197 + 15   203 − 24

Make up your own sums that balance.

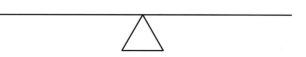

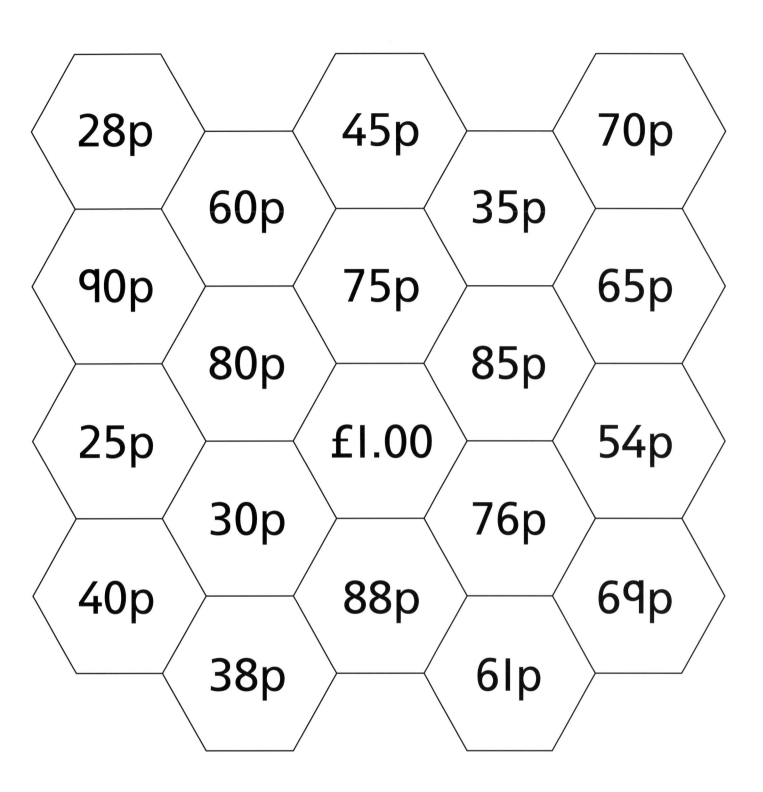

28p

45p

70p

60p

35p

90p

75p

65p

80p

85p

25p

£1.00

54p

30p

76p

40p

88p

69p

38p

61p

$\dfrac{1}{2}$	$\dfrac{2}{4}$	$\dfrac{3}{6}$	$\dfrac{3}{4}$	$\dfrac{4}{8}$
$\dfrac{1}{3}$	$\dfrac{2}{6}$	$\dfrac{3}{9}$	$\dfrac{2}{3}$	$\dfrac{4}{6}$
$\dfrac{1}{10}$	$\dfrac{2}{10}$	$\dfrac{1}{4}$	$\dfrac{10}{20}$	$\dfrac{1}{5}$
$\dfrac{5}{10}$	$\dfrac{2}{8}$	$\dfrac{5}{20}$	$\dfrac{10}{30}$	$\dfrac{2}{20}$
$\dfrac{20}{30}$	$\dfrac{30}{40}$	$\dfrac{6}{9}$	$\dfrac{1}{2}$	$\dfrac{2}{4}$

365	298	101	531	1000
461	102	428	875	785
937	537	857	124	482
578	793	379	236	364
121	753	375	119	197
623	811	643	1015	909
350	305	705	507	205

| larger than | smaller than |
| more than | less than |

two hundred and two	six hundred and eighty-one	three hundred and fifty-six	seven hundred and twenty	five hundred and seven
two hundred and five	one hundred and forty-two	four hundred and sixty-four	nine hundred and nineteen	eight hundred and twelve
one hundred and seventy-nine	nine hundred and ninety-one	one hundred and seven	two hundred and sixteen	three hundred and twelve
four hundred and fifty-five	five hundred and nineteen	six hundred and one	seven hundred and forty-five	eight hundred and thirty-six
nine hundred and twenty-three	one hundred and eighty-eight	two hundred and forty	three hundred and eight	four hundred and twelve
five hundred and sixty-three	six hundred and one	seven hundred and fifteen	eight hundred and twenty-one	nine hundred and ninety-nine
one hundred and twenty-three	two hundred and eighty-four	three hundred and seventy-one	four hundred and twenty-one	five hundred

larger than	smaller than
more than	less than

Corner numbers

Add the numbers in circles on each hexagon, then subtract the number in a square from your answer.

Put the total in the centre of the hexagon.

e.g.
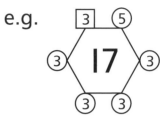

$(3+3+3+3+5-3)$

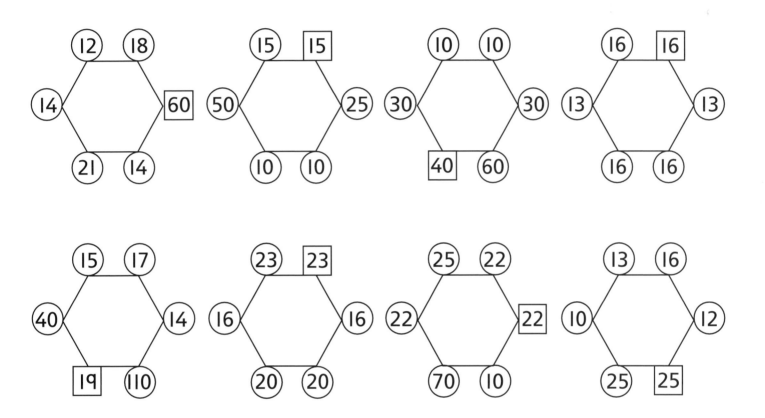

Now put your own numbers on the corners to make the total in the centre of the hexagon.

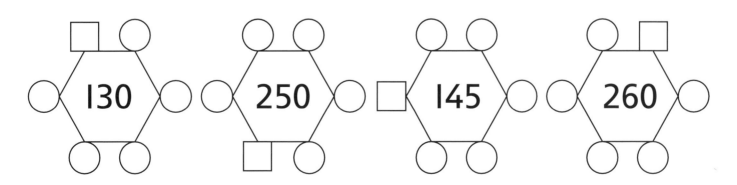

Travel from top to bottom using + −.

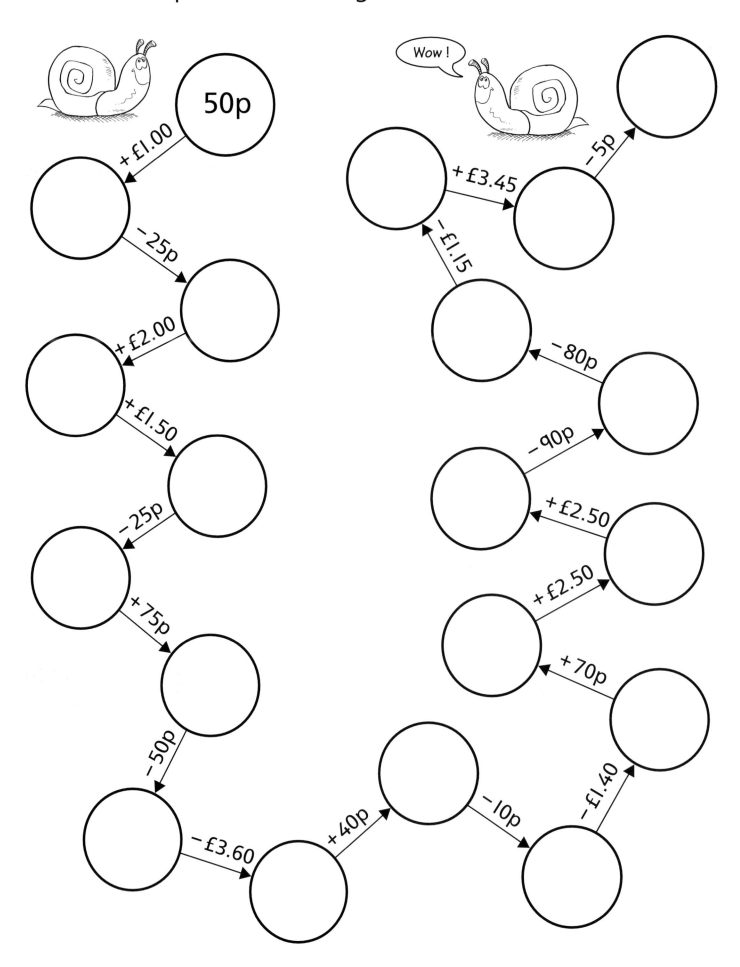

Wow!

50p

+£1.00

−25p

+£2.00

+£1.50

−25p

+75p

−50p

−£3.60

+40p

−10p

−£1.40

+70p

+£2.50

+£2.50

−90p

−80p

−£1.15

+£3.45

−5p

Clocks

Put in hands.

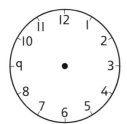

7 o'clock

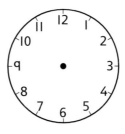

3:45

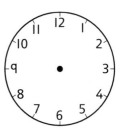

2:30

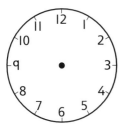

9 o'clock

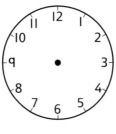

6:15

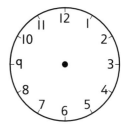

7:30

Write the digital times.

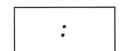

quarter past eight

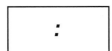

half past five

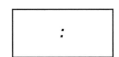

quarter to one

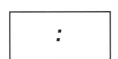

ten past two

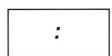

half past nine

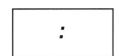

six o'clock

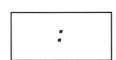

twenty past five

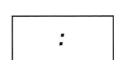

twenty to three

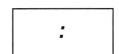

12 o'clock

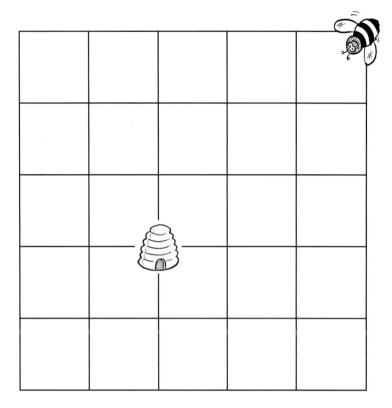

Our bee would like to get to his hive. He can only travel W and S.

Find different routes for him and write them down like this:

S. S. S. W. W. W.

Choose a new position for the hive.
How many different routes are there now?

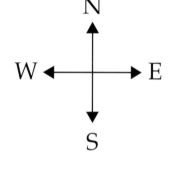

N

W ← → E

S

This time the bee can only travel N and E.

How many different routes could he take?
Write them down.

Number maze

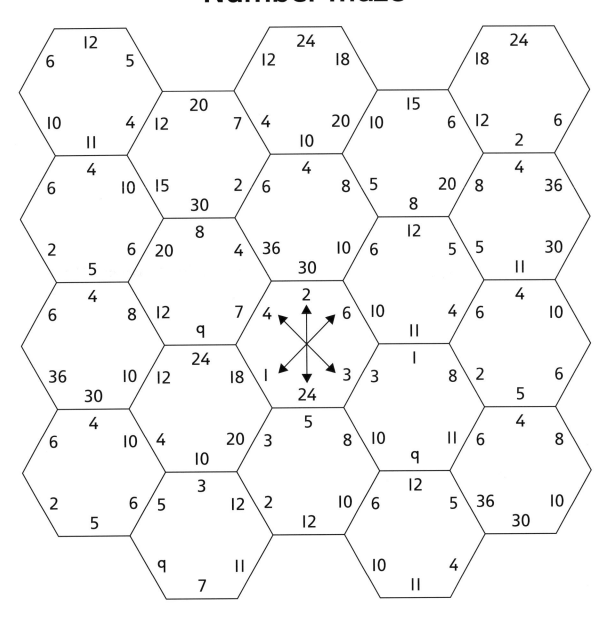

Play this game with a partner.

You will need two dice and two counters in different colours. Place the counters at the start point on the arrows. Take it in turns to throw both the dice and add, multiply, subtract or divide your two scores to make one of the numbers in the hexagon. Follow that number into the next hexagon, moving your counter to mark your place. Keep taking turns until someone reaches the edge of the maze.

The first to escape is the winner.

How many throws to escape?

PCM 31

Cut the pieces out, and put them together to make a spiral
100 square.

Stick the square into your book.

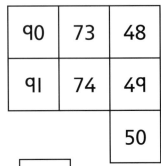

90	73	48
91	74	49
		50

64	65
63	84

55	54		
24	23	22	21

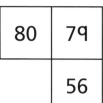

80	79
	56
	25

2	3	4	5
		39	40

70

6	7	8	9	10

1
36	37	38
35
34

33	62
32	61

31	60	81	94
30	59
29	58

11
45	12
46	13
47	14

15
16
17
51	18
20	19

66	67
85	86

57
28	27	26

83	96
82	95

41	42	43	44
68	69

93	92		
78	77	76	75
		53	52

87	88	71
97	98	89	72
100	99

Millipedes

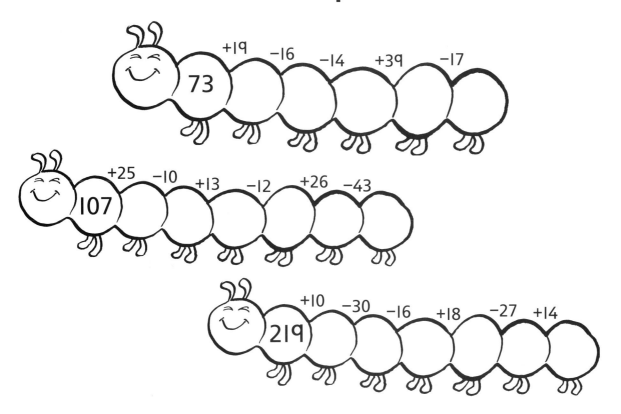

Now fill in your own millipedes.

Start with a 3-digit number and use + and − and 2-digit numbers to make the chain.

A

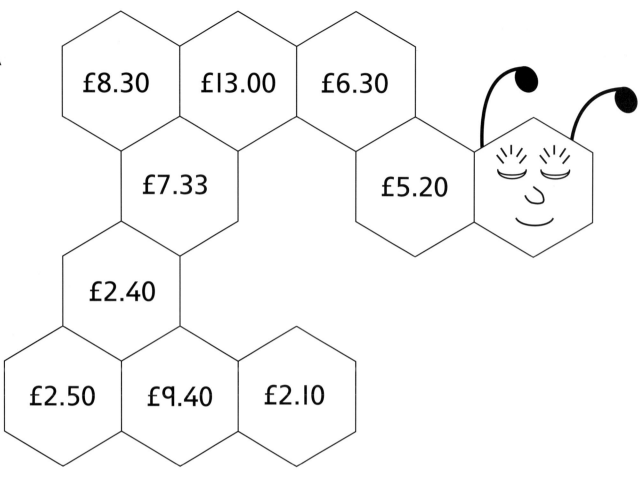

£8.30 £13.00 £6.30

£7.33 £5.20

£2.40

£2.50 £9.40 £2.10

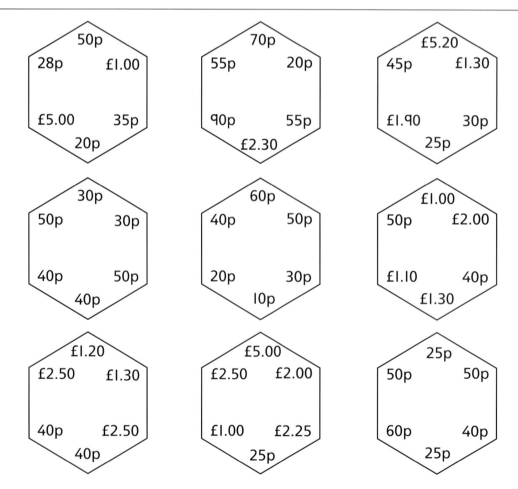

50p		
28p		£1.00
£5.00		35p
	20p	

70p		
55p		20p
90p		55p
	£2.30	

£5.20		
45p		£1.30
£1.90		30p
	25p	

30p		
50p		30p
40p		50p
	40p	

60p		
40p		50p
20p		30p
	10p	

£1.00		
50p		£2.00
£1.10		40p
	£1.30	

£1.20		
£2.50		£1.30
40p		£2.50
	40p	

£5.00		
£2.50		£2.00
£1.00		£2.25
	25p	

25p		
50p		50p
60p		40p
	25p	

B

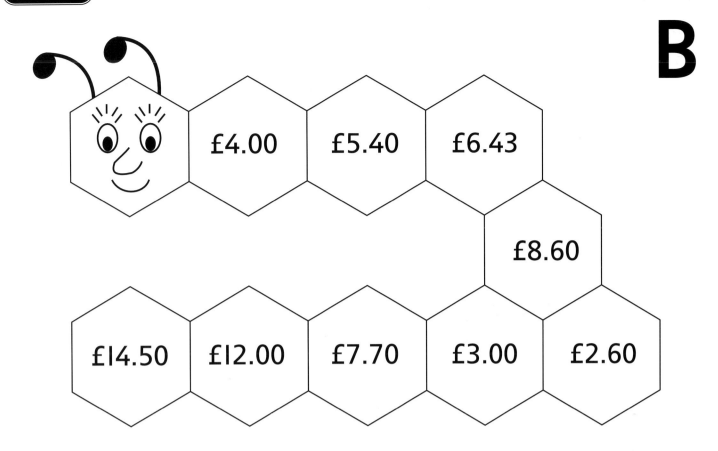

£4.00   £5.40   £6.43

£8.60

£14.50   £12.00   £7.70   £3.00   £2.60

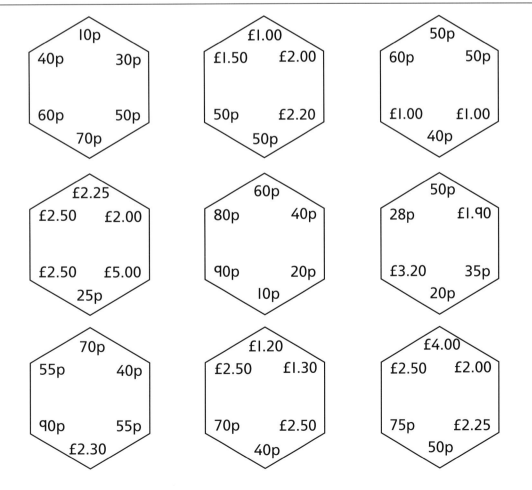

	10p	
40p		30p
60p		50p
	70p	

£1.00		
£1.50		£2.00
50p		£2.20
	50p	

	50p	
60p		50p
£1.00		£1.00
	40p	

£2.25		
£2.50		£2.00
£2.50		£5.00
	25p	

	60p	
80p		40p
90p		20p
	10p	

	50p	
28p		£1.90
£3.20		35p
	20p	

	70p	
55p		40p
90p		55p
	£2.30	

£1.20		
£2.50		£1.30
70p		£2.50
	40p	

	£4.00	
£2.50		£2.00
75p		£2.25
	50p	

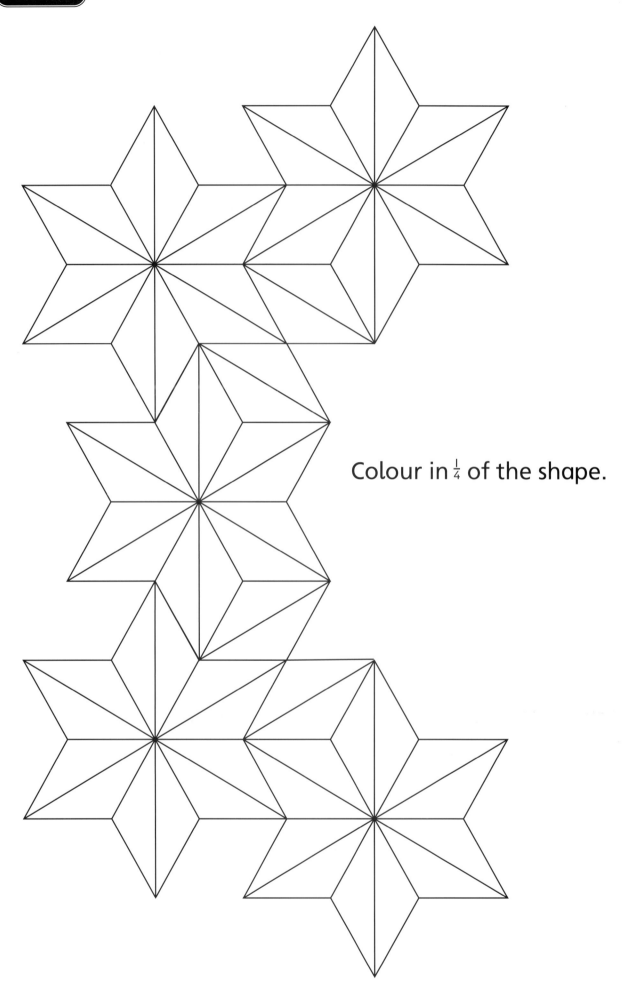

Colour in $\frac{1}{4}$ of the shape.

Add all the numbers. Write the total in the centre.

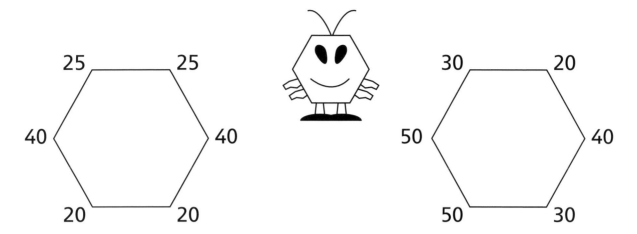

25   25

40   40

20   20

30   20

50   40

50   30

Start with the circle number. Follow the instructions round clockwise. Write the total in the centre.

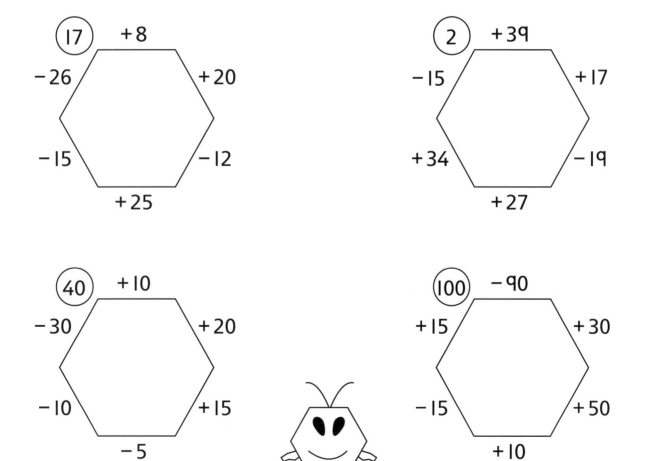

17   + 8

− 26   + 20

− 15   − 12

+ 25

2   + 39

− 15   + 17

+ 34   − 19

+ 27

40   + 10

− 30   + 20

− 10   + 15

− 5

100   − 90

+ 15   + 30

− 15   + 50

+ 10

Can you make up your own sums on the alien sheet?

This is a time line.

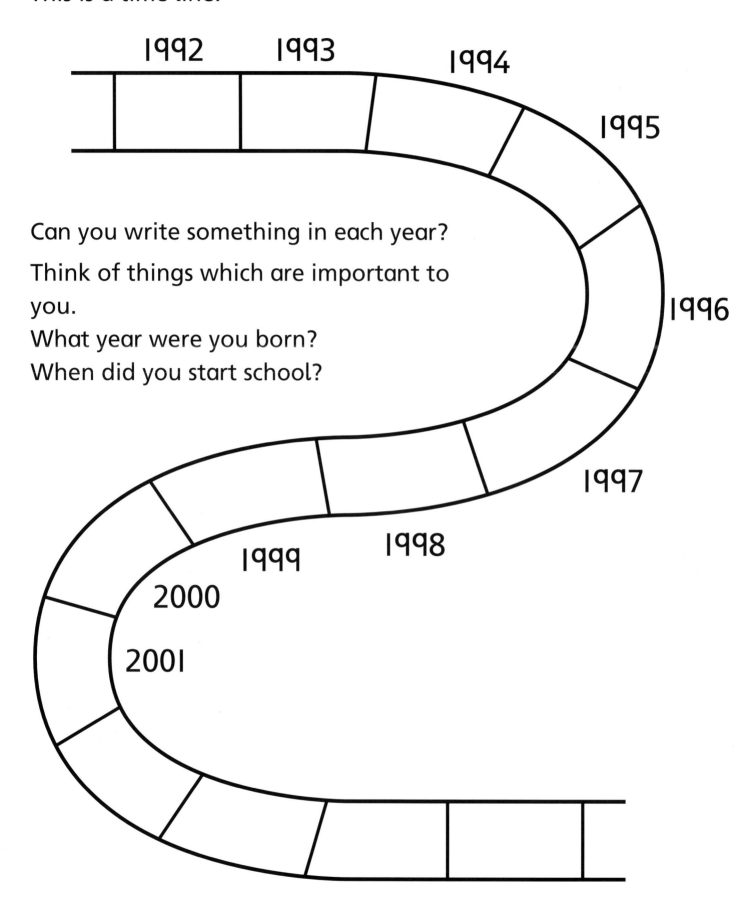

Can you write something in each year?

Think of things which are important to you.

What year were you born?

When did you start school?

1992 1993 1994 1995 1996 1997 1998 1999 2000 2001

National Numeracy Strategy Teaching Objectives

The following chart demonstrates which Maths Pyramid units are most suited to help you to develop and broaden the children's knowledge of the relevant Framework for Teaching Mathematics objectives. As Maths Pyramid is aimed at more able children, it must be noted that on occasion the content of the teaching inputs will necessarily go further than explicitly required by the Framework.

✔ = coverage throughout Maths Pyramid

Numbers and the number system Counting, properties of numbers and number sequences	*Maths Pyramid Units*
Count larger collections by grouping them: for example, in tens, then other numbers.	✔
Describe and extend number sequences: count on or back in tens or hundreds, starting from any two- or three-digit number;	1, 2, 7, 19, 30
count on or back in twos starting from any two-digit number, and recognise odd and even numbers to at least 100;	7, 19
count on in steps of 3, 4 or 5 from any small number to at least 50, then back again.	7, 19
Recognise two-digit and three-digit multiples of 2, 5 or 10, and three-digit multiples of 50 and 100.	7, 30
Place value and ordering	
Read and write whole numbers to at least 1000 in figures and words.	1, 13, 24, ✔
Know what each digit represents, and partition three-digit numbers into a multiple of 100, a multiple of ten and ones (HTU).	1, 11, 13
Read and begin to write the vocabulary of comparing and ordering numbers, including ordinal numbers to at least 100. Compare two given three-digit numbers, say which is more or less, and give a number which lies between them.	1, 13, 24
Say the number that is 1, 10 or 100 more or less than any given two- or three-digit number.	1
Order whole numbers to at least 1000, and position them on a number line.	1, 24
Estimating and rounding	
Read and begin to write the vocabulary of estimation and approximation.	✔
Give a sensible estimate of up to about 100 objects	✔
Round any two-digit number to the nearest 10 and any three-digit number to the nearest 100.	24
Fractions	
Recognise unit fractions such as 1/2, 1/3, 1/4, 1/5, 1/10… and use them to find fractions of shapes and numbers.	10, 22, 33
Begin to recognise simple fractions that are several parts of a whole, such as 3/4, 2/3 or 3/10.	10, 22, 33
Begin to recognise simple equivalent fractions: for example, five tenths and one half, five fifths and one whole.	10, 22, 33
Compare familiar fractions: for example, know that on the number line one half lies between one quarter and three quarters.	22, 33
Estimate a simple fraction.	13, 33

Calculations Understanding addition and subtraction	
Extend understanding of the operations of addition and subtraction, read and begin to write the related vocabulary, and continue to recognise that addition can be done in any order.	2, 11, 14, 20, 25, 32
Use the +, − and = signs	2, 14, 20, 25
Extend understanding that more than two numbers can be added, add three or four single-digit numbers mentally, or three or four two-digit numbers with the help of apparatus or pencil and paper.	2, 7, 9, 20, 25
Extend understanding that subtraction is the inverse of addition.	2, 20
Rapid recall of addition and subtraction facts	
Know by heart: all addition and subtraction facts for each number to 20;	25
all pairs of multiples of 100 with a total of 1000 (e.g. 300 + 700)	✔
Derive quickly: all pairs of multiples of 5 with a total of 100 (e.g. 35 + 65).	✔

Mental calculation strategies (+ and −)	
Use knowledge that addition can be done in any order to do mental calculations more efficiently. For example: put the larger number first and count on; add three or four small numbers by putting the largest number first and/or by finding pairs totalling 9, 10 or 11; partition into '5 and a bit' when adding 6, 7, 8 or 9 (e.g. $47 + 8 = 45 + 2 + 5 + 3 = 50 + 5 = 55$); partition into tens and units, then recombine (e.g. $34 + 53 = 30 + 50 + 4 + 3$).	11, 20, 25, 34
Find a small difference by counting up from the smaller to the larger number (e.g. $102 − 97$).	11, 20, 25
Identify near doubles, using doubles already known (e.g. $80 + 81$).	25, 32
Add and subtract mentally a 'near multiple of 10' to or from a two-digit number... by adding or subtracting 10, 20, 30... and adjusting.	2, 14
Use patterns of similar calculations.	14
Say or write a subtraction statement corresponding to a given addition statement, and vice versa.	20
Use known number facts and place value to add/subtract mentally.	11, 32
Bridge through a multiple of 10, then adjust.	14, 20, ✔
Pencil and paper procedures (+ and −)	
Use informal pencil and paper methods to support, record or explain HTU ± TU, HTU ± HTU.	25
Begin to use column addition and subtraction for HTU ± TU where the calculation cannot easily be done mentally.	34
Understanding multiplication and division	
Understand multiplication as repeated addition. Read and begin to write the related vocabulary. Extend understanding that multiplication can be done in any order.	8, 21, 31
Understand division as grouping (repeated subtraction) or sharing. Read and begin to write the related vocabulary.	8, 31
Recognise that division is the inverse of multiplication, and that halving is the inverse of doubling.	21, 31
Begin to find remainders after simple division.	31
Round up or down after division, depending on the context.	29
Rapid recall of multiplication and division facts	
Know by heart: Multiplication facts for the 2, 5 and 10 times-tables.	7, 8
Begin to know the 3 and 4 times-table.	7, 19
Derive quickly: division facts corresponding to the 2, 5 and 10 times-tables; doubles of all whole numbers to at least 20 (e.g. $17 + 17$ or 17×2); doubles of multiples of 5 to 100 (e.g. 75×2, 90×2); doubles of multiples of 50 to 500 (e.g. 450×2); and all the corresponding halves (e.g. $36 \div 2$, half of 130, $900 \div 2$).	2, 30, 31, ✔
Mental calculation strategies (× and ÷)	
To multiply by 10, 100, shift the digits one/two places to the left.	30, 31
Use doubling or halving, starting from known facts (e.g. 8×4 is double 4×4).	3
Say or write a division statement corresponding to a given multiplication statement.	21, 31
Use known number facts and place value to carry out mentally simple multiplications and divisions.	8, 31
Checking results of calculations	
Check subtraction with addition, halving with doubling and division with multiplication.	20, 21, 31, 32
Repeat addition or multiplication in a different order.	8, 21, 31, ✔
Check with an equivalent calculation.	31, ✔

Solving problems **Making decisions**	
Choose and use appropriate operations (including multiplication and division) to solve word problems and appropriate ways of calculating: mental, mental with jottings, pencil and paper.	32

Reasoning about numbers or shapes	
Solve mathematical problems or puzzles, recognise simple patterns and relationships, generalise and predict. Suggest extensions by asking 'What if …?'	6, 7, 19, 29, 30
Investigate a general statement about familiar numbers or shapes by finding examples that satisfy it.	7
Explain methods and reasoning orally and, where appropriate, in writing.	6, 19, 29
Problems involving 'real life', money and measures	
Solve word problems involving numbers in 'real life', money and measures, using one or more steps, including finding totals and giving change, and working out which coins to pay.	3, 9, 15, 21, 26, 27
Explain how the problem was solved.	9, 32
Recognise all coins and notes. Understand and use £.p notation (for example, know that £3.06 is £3 and 6p).	9, 15, 21

Handling data
Organising and using data

Solve a given problem by organising and interpreting numerical data in simple lists, tables and graphs, for example: simple frequency tables; pictograms – symbol representing two units; bar charts – intervals labelled in ones then twos; Venn and Carroll diagrams (one criterion).	12, 23, 35

Measures, shape and space
Measures

Read and begin to write the vocabulary related to length, mass and capacity.	4, 16, 27
Measure and compare using standard units (km, m, cm, kg, g, l, ml), including using a ruler to draw and measure lines to the nearest half centimetre.	4, 16, 27
Know the relationships between kilometres and metres, metres and centimetres, kilograms and grams, litres and millilitres.	4, 16, 27
Begin to use decimal notation for metres and centimetres.	27
Suggest suitable units and measuring equipment to estimate or measure length, mass or capacity.	4, 16, 27
Read scales to the nearest division (labelled or unlabelled).	4, 16, 27
Record estimates and measurements to the nearest whole or half unit (e.g. 'about 3.5 kg'), or in mixed units (e.g. '3 m and 20 cm').	4, 16, 27
Read and begin to write the vocabulary related to time.	4, 11
Use units of time and know the relationships between them (second, minute, hour, day, week, month, year). Suggest suitable units to estimate or measure time.	4, 11, 16, 27, 32
Use a calendar. Read the time to 5 minutes on an analogue clock and a 12-hour digital clock and use the notation 9:40.	4
Shape and space	
Classify and describe 3-D and 2-D shapes, including the hemisphere, prism, semi-circle, quadrilateral… referring to properties such as reflective symmetry (2-D), the number or shapes of faces, the number of sides, edges and vertices, whether sides/edges are the same length, whether or not angles are right angles …	5, 17, 18, 28
Make and describe shapes and patterns: for example, explore the different shapes that can be made from four cubes.	5, 17, 18
Relate solid shapes to pictures of them.	28
Identify and sketch lines of symmetry in simple shapes, and recognise shapes with no lines of symmetry.	5, 18
Sketch the reflection of a simple shape in a mirror line along one edge.	5, 18
Read and begin to write the vocabulary related to position, direction and movement: for example, describe and find the position of a square on a grid of squares with the rows and columns labelled.	28
Recognise and use the four compass directions N, S, E, W.	28
Make and describe right-angled turns, including turns between the four compass points.	17
Identify right angles in 2-D shapes and the environment.	17
Recognise that a straight line is equivalent to two right angles.	17
Compare angles with a right angle.	17

Match to Published Maths Schemes

Maths Pyramid has been designed for ease of use either with a whole class or a small group of children, alongside your chosen maths scheme, whether that is a commercial or a privately-developed one. The following chart provides you with guidance on how to extend the following schemes with Maths Pyramid:

- Cambridge Primary Mathematics (Module 4) – referenced to unit name and number.
- Original Abacus– referenced to unit number.
- STEPS Mathematics– referenced to level and unit number.
- Nelson Mathematics – referenced to Towards Level, chapter title and unit number.

- National Curriculum Ginn Mathematics – referenced to level and stage number.
- Heinemann Maths – referenced to level and page number.

The references are those provided in each case by the relevant publisher, and as such should be familiar to users. Maths Pyramid is not designed exactly to match these schemes, but to match the Framework for Teaching Mathematics, so for each Maths Pyramid unit we have suggested several different sections of each scheme, where possible, from which you may select.

Maths Pyramid Objectives	CPM	Abacus	STEPS	Nelson	NCGM	HM
Unit 1 – Place value and ordering (3 days) To read and write whole numbers to at least 1000 in figures and words and know what each digit represents. To order whole numbers to at least 1000. Count on or back in hundreds. Compare two given 3-digit numbers, say which is more or less and give a number which lies between them.	Number 1, 2, 6, 7, 11, 12	N1, N2, N30, N31, R1, R8	3a: 5, 17 3b: 10	TL2 Numbers to 100 U2, 8, 9; Patterns U5 TL3 Numbers to 1000 U1–5	48–9, 51, 67	3: 198 4: 26–7, 34–47
Unit 2 – Understanding +, − , mental calculation strategies (5 days) To extend understanding of the operations of addition and subtraction and that more than two numbers can be added. To read and begin to write the vocabulary of addition. To use known number facts and place value to add/subtract mentally. To use the +, − and = signs.	Number 1, 2, 6, 7, 11, 12	N6, N10, N11, N12, N13, N14, N15, N18, R2, R4, R5	3a: 7, 9, 27, 30	TL2 Addition and Subtraction U1–5; Addition and Subtraction Facts to 10 U1–5; Numbers to 20 U4, 5; Numbers to 100 U5, 7–9 TL3 Addition and Subtraction to 100 U1–9.	1–3, 9, 13, 16, 17, 32	3: 52, 58–9, 66–8, 70, 74–6
Unit 3 – Money and 'real life' problems, making decisions, checking results (5 days) To choose and use appropriate operations (including × and ÷). To solve problems involving numbers in 'real life'. To use doubling or halving, starting from known facts.	Money 1, 2, 3	N7, N22	3a: 10, 36 3b: 17 4a: 3	TL3 Addition and Subtraction to 100 U2, 4, 5, 7; Numbers to 1000 U9; Multiplication and Division U1–5; Money U1, 4–7; Multiplication U3–8; Division U1, 2	6–8, 17, 33, 35, 41, 45	3: 60–63, 76–9, 104–106 4: 142–151
Unit 4 – Measures, including problems (5 days) To read scales to the nearest division. To measure and compare using standard units To use record estimates and measurements to the nearest whole or half unit or in mixed units. To suggest suitable units and measuring equipment. To use units of time and know the relationship between them	Length 1, 2, 3; Weight 1, 2, 3; Volume and capacity 1, 2; Time 3	M8, M9, R9	3a: 6, 11, 15, 20, 22, 25, 34, 37, 40	TL2 Length U2; Weight U2; Capacity U2 TL3 Length U1–5; Weight U1–4; Capacity U1–4	3, 26, 2	3: 134–145, 148–154, 159–160, 162–4, 166 4: 178–182, 190–97, 200–217, 221
Unit 5 – Shape and space (4 days) To classify and describe 2D and 3D shapes according to their properties. To make and describe shapes and patterns, identify and sketch lines of symmetry in simple shapes and recognise shapes with no lines of symmetry.	Shape 1, 2, 3	S1, S2, S3, S4, S5	2: 4 3a: 19, 20, 21, 38 3b: 24	TL2 3D Shapes U4, 5; 2D Shapes U1–5 TL3 3D Shapes U1, 2, 4; 2D Shapes U1–6		3: 169–172, 181, 186–89 4: 227–236, 243–7
Unit 6 – Reasoning about shapes (4 days) To solve mathematical problems or puzzles, explain methods and discuss reasoning. To recognise simple patterns and relationships.	Opportunities throughout	Opportunities throughout	3a and 3b, opportunities throughout	TL3, opportunities throughout		3: 43, 183, 199

Maths Pyramid Objectives	CPM	Abacus	STEPS	Nelson	NCGM	HM
Unit 7 – Counting and properties of number, reasoning about numbers (5 days) To solve mathematical problems and explain methods. To recognise familiar multiples. To investigate general statements about familiar numbers. To describe and extend number sequences. To count on or back in a variety of ways.	Number 1, 2, 3, 6, 7, 8, 9	N15, N16, N27, N28, R3, R4, R5, R7	3b: 3, 5, 18, 22	TL3, opportunities throughout		3: 128 4: 34–47
Unit 8 – Understanding ×, ÷, mental calculation strategies (5 days) To know by heart multiplication facts for the 2, 5 10 times–tables. To understand multiplication as repeated addition and extend understanding that it can be done in any order. To understand division as grouping. To use known number facts to carry out mentally simple multiplication or division.	Number 3, 4, 8,	N8, N9, N21, N25, R3, R6	3a: 24 3b: 3, 8, 22, 27 4a: 1, 3	TL3 Multiplication U1–8; Multiplication and Division U1, 2, 5; Number Patterns U3, 4		3: 87–94, 101–102, 104, 111–114, 116, 123–5
Unit 9 – Money and 'real life' problems, making decisions, checking results (5 days) To solve problems involving numbers and money. To explain methods orally and in writing. To understand and use £.p notation.	Money 1, 2, 3	Opportunities throughout	3a: 10, 36 3b: 17	TL3 Money U1–7	6, 7, 8, 17, 33, 35, 41, 45	3: 60–63, 76–9, 104–106 4: 142–151
Unit 10 – Fractions (5 days) To recognise unit fractions and use them to find fractions of shapes and numbers. To begin to recognise simple fractions that are several parts of a whole. To begin to recognise simple equivalent fractions.	Number 5, 10, 15	N6, N12, N23, N2	3a: 23, 3b: 12	TL2 Multiplication and Division U3, 4; TL3 Division U1–4	52	3: 118–121 4: 154–165
Unit 11 – Understanding +, −, time, including problems, making decisions, checking results (5 days) To use known number facts to add and subtract mentally. To use knowledge that addition can be done in any order to do mental calculations more efficiently. To read and begin to write the vocabulary related to time.	Number 11 (TRB); Number 1, 2, 6; Time 1, 2, 3	M8, M9, N10, N11, N12, N13, N14, N15, N18, R5, R9	3a: 7, 9, 22, 27, 40	TL2 Time U1, 2, 6, 7 TL3 Addition and Subtraction to 100 U3–7; Time U12;	1-3, 17, 32, 46, 47	3: 57–8, 67–8, 134–145 4: 29–33, 200–217
Unit 12 – Handling data (5 days) To use Venn and Carroll diagrams to organise and interpret data.	Data 1, 3	N12, N21		TL2 Handling Data U3-5, 8 TL3 Handling Data U2–5		
Unit 13 – Place value, ordering, estimating and rounding, (3 days) To know what each digit represents and partition numbers. To compare two given 3-digit numbers, say which is more or less and give a number which lies between them.	Number 1, 2, 6, 7, 11, 12	N10, N13, N17, R1, R8	3a: 7 3b: 25	TL2 Numbers to 100 U1, 3 TL3 Numbers to 1000 U1, 2, 3, 5	48, 51, 67	4: 37–44
Unit 14 – Understanding + and −, mental calculation strategies (5 days) To extend understanding that subtraction is the inverse of addition. To read and begin to write the vocabulary of subtraction. To add or subtract mentally a 'near multiple of 10' to or from a 2-digit number. To use patterns of similar calculations. To bridge through a multiple of 10, then adjust.	Number 1, 2, 6, 7, 11, 12	N10, N13, N17, R1, R8	3a: 7 3b: 25	TL2 Exploring Addition and Subtraction U1–5 TL3 Addition and Subtraction to 100 U1–7, 9	30, 31, 32, 34, 50, 53, 54, 55, 8	3: 52–53, 58–59, 66–70, 74–6 4: 29–30, 91, 169
Unit 15 – Money and 'real life' problems, making decisions, checking results (5 days) To solve word problems involving numbers in real life using one or more steps. To use £.p notation and convert from pence to pounds and vice versa.	Money 1, 2, 3	Opportunities throughout	3a: 10, 36 3b: 17	TL3 Money U1–7	6, 7, 8, 17, 33, 35, 41, 45	3: 60–63, 76–9, 104–106 4: 142–151

Maths Pyramid Objectives	CPM	Abacus	STEPS	Nelson	NCGM	HM
Unit 16 – Measures and time, including problems (5 days) To solve word problems involving measures. To use a ruler to measure lines to the nearest half centimetre. To record estimates and measurements to the nearest whole or half unit and check the accuracy of estimates. To suggest suitable units for all measuring activities. To read accurately analogue and digital clocks.	Volume and capacity 2 Length 2, 3 Weight 3 Time 1, 3	M1, M2, M4, M5, M7, M8	3a: 6, 11, 15, 20, 22, 25, 34, 37, 40	All TL2 and TL3 units in Length, Weight and Capacity, and Time	23, 26, 27, 46, 47	3: 134 – 145, 159–160, 162–4, 166 4: 178–182, 190–197, 200–217, 219–221
Unit 17 – Shape and space (3 days) To describe and classify 2D and 3D shapes according to their properties. To make and describe 3D shapes. To identify right angles in 2D shapes and in the environment. To understand angle as a measure of turn.	Shape 1, 2 Angles 3	R10, S1, S2, S3, S4	3a: 19, 21, 38 3b: 24, 29	TL2 3D Shapes U5; 2D Shapes U3, 4; TL3 3D Shapes U1, 2, 4; 2D Shapes U1, 2, 4–6	61, 62	3: 169–172, 178–181 4: 227–236, 257–263
Unit 18 – Reasoning about shapes and space (5 days) To recognise line symmetry. To identify and sketch symmetrical patterns.	Shape 3	S5	2: 4 3a: 2, 20	TL2 Moving Geometry U5, 6; 2D shapes U5; TL3 U6		3: 186–9 4: 243–7
Unit 19 – Counting and properties of number, reasoning about numbers (5 days) To count on or back in tens and hundreds from any two- or three- digit number. To recognise odd and even numbers to 100. To investigate patterns and relationships, generalise, predict and explain.	Number 1, 2, 6, 7, 8	N: 15, N28, R4, R5, R7	3a: 5, 14, 16, 18 3b: 37, 39	TL2 Numbers to 100 U2, 8, 9; Patterns U5; TL3 Addition and Subtraction to 100 U1	57	3: 128 4: 34–47
Unit 20 – Understanding + and −, mental calculation strategies (5 days) To add three 2-digit numbers. To use knowledge that numbers can be added in any order to do mental calculations more efficiently. To find, describe and use patterns of similar calculations. To extend understanding that subtraction is the inverse of addition.	Number 1, 2, 6, 7, 11, 12	N13, N17, R2, R4, R7	3a: 7, 16, 27 3b: 11, 25	TL2 Multiplication and Division U3, 4; TL3 Division U1–4	30, 31, 32, 34, 50, 53, 54, 55, 58	3: 52, 58, 59, 66-8, 70, 74-6 4: 169-70
Unit 21 – Understanding ×, ÷, money and 'real life' problems (5 days) To recognise all coins, find totals and give change. To use all four operations as appropriate to solve real life problems. To extend understanding that multiplication can be done in any order. To understand that division is the inverse of multiplication.	Money 1, 2, 3 Number 3, 4, 8	N4, N26	3a: 1, 10, 24, 36 3b: 17	TL3 Money U1–7; Addition and Subtraction to 100 U2, 4, 5, 7; Multiplication and Division U1–5	17	3:60–63, 76–9, 106 4: 142–151
Unit 22 – Fractions (5 days) To recognise and find simple fractions of shapes and numbers. To create models illustrating simple fractions. To compare simple fractions and order them. To position fractions on a number line.	Number 10, 15 N23, N24	3a: 23 3b: 12	TL2 Multiplication and Division U3, 4; TL3	Division U1–4	52	3:118–121 4: 154–165
Unit 23 – Handling data (5 days) To collect and sort information and display it in lists and Venn and Carroll diagrams. To interpret the diagrams, answer questions and make statements using them.	Data 1, 3	D1, D2, D3, N12, N21	3a: 4			3: 196–7 4: 268–284
Unit 24 – Place value, ordering and rounding (3 days) To round numbers to the nearest 10. To order whole numbers in words and figures. To read the vocabulary of comparing and ordering numbers. To identify which of a given set of numbers is nearest to another given number.	Number 12	N4	3a: 5, 17 3b: 10	TL2 Numbers to 100 U4; TL3 Numbers to 1000 U6, 7	49, 56	3: 50–51 4: 27–8

Maths Pyramid Objectives	CPM	Abacus	STEPS	Nelson	NCGM	HM
Unit 25 – Understanding + and –, mental calculation strategies (5 days) To know and use addition and subtraction facts for each number to 20. To use informal pencil and paper procedures to add large sets of numbers. To identify doubles and near doubles of numbers up to 1000.	Number 1, 2, 6, 7, 11, 12	N3, N5, N19, N20, N28, N29, R2	3a: 14, 16, 18, 27, 30 3b: 25, 28	TL3 Addition and Subtraction to 100 U6	4, 5, 17, 30, 31, 34, 53, 54	3: 26–43, 52–7 4: 30–31
Unit 26 – Money and 'real life' problems (5 days) To use pencil and paper procedures to solve real life problems with more than one step. To use all four operations in the context of money.	Money 1, 2, 3	Opportunities throughout	3a: 10, 27, 30, 36 3b: 17	TL3 Money U1–7	6, 7, 8, 17, 33, 35, 41, 45	3: 60–63, 76–9 4: 142–151
Unit 27 – Measures, including problems (5 days) To solve problems involving measures. To use a range of measuring equipment and read scales accurately to the nearest division. To record estimates and measures in mixed units. To compare measurements and estimates. To use the relationships between units of time	Length 2, 3 Weight 2, 3 Volume and Capacity 2 Time 3	M1, M2, M4, M5, M7, M8, M9, R9	3a: 6, 11, 15, 20, 22, 25, 34, 37, 40	TL2 Time, U1, 2, 6, 7; TL3 Length U4, 5; Weight U2, 3; Capacity U3, 4; Time U1, 2, 4	23, 26, 27	3: 148–154, 159–160, 162–4, 166 4: 178–182, 190–197, 219–21
Unit 28 – Shape and space (4 days) To use mathematical terms to identify and describe 2D and 3D shapes. To make and describe right-angled turns. To describe and find positions on a grid. To know and use the four compass directions.	Shape 1, 2 Angles 3	S1, S2, S3, S4, S6, S7, S9	3a: 8, 19, 21 3b: 4, 14	TL2 3D Shapes U5; 2D Shapes U3, 4; TL3 3D Shapes U1, 2, 4; 2D Shapes U1, 2, 4, 5, 6		3: 169–172, 178–181 4: 227–236, 238–40, 261–3
Unit 29 – Reasoning (4 days) To solve mathematical puzzles and carry out investigations requiring a methodical approach. To explain methods of calculation. To recognise patterns and relationships and ask questions.	Oppotunities througout	Opportunities throughout	3a: 18 3b: 37, 39		17	3: 43, 183, 199
Unit 30 – Counting and properties of number, reasoning about numbers (5 days) To recognise and extend number sequences and patterns . To complete sequences with 'missing' numbers. To count on or back in steps of various sizes from any 3-digit number. To recognise two- and 3-digit multiples of 2, 5 and 10.	Number 1, 2, 3, 6, 7, 8 R3, R4, R5, R7	N15, N16, N28	3a: 5, 18 3b: 3, 22		37, 46, 50	3: 128 4: 34–47
Unit 31 – Understanding ×, ÷, mental calculation strategies (5 days) To recognise that division is the inverse of multiplication and halving is the inverse of doubling. To find remainders after simple division. To check results with an equivalent calculation.	Number 4, 7	N26	3a: 24 3b: 6, 7 4a: 3			3: 114–115, 125–6 4: 121–7
Unit 32 – Money and 'real life' problems, making decisions, checking results (5 days) To solve more complex real life problems using appropriate operations, check results and explain how the problem was solved	Money 1, 2, 3	Opportunities throughout	3a: 10, 18, 36 3b: 17, 37, 39		17	3: 60–63, 76–9 4: 142–151
Unit 33 – Fractions (5 days) To find simple fractions of lwhole numbers up to 20. To recognise patterns in fractions of odd and even numbers. To find equivalents of non-unit fractions. To begin to use fractions in real life problems.	Number 5, 10, 15	N23, N24	3a: 23 3b: 12	TL2 Multiplication and division U3, 4 TL3 Division U1–4	52	3: 118–121 4: 154–165

Maths Pyramid Objectives	CPM	Abacus	STEPS	Nelson	NCGM	HM
Unit 34 – Understanding + and –, paper and pencil procedures and problems, including time (5 days) To use number patterns, mental strategies and rapid recall of number facts to perform mental calculations in an efficient manner. To construct a timeline spanning several years. To read and interpret timetables.	Number 1, 2, 6, 7	N3, N5, N17, R2	3b: 25, 28	TL2 Numbers to 100 U6; TL3 Multiplication and Division U4, 5; Money U6, 7; Numbers to 1000 U9, 10	53, 54	
Unit 35 – Data (5 days) To collect data with the purpose of testing a hypothesis. To display data in lists, charts, Venn and Carroll diagrams and bar charts. To use the displays to draw conclusions. To consider extensions and the possible wider uses of their information.	Data 1, 3	D1, D2, D3, N12, N21	3a: 4	TL2 Handling Data U3–5, 8 TL3 Handling Data U2–5	61, 62	3: 196–7 4: 268–284

Northern Ireland Lines of Development

The following chart gives you an at-a-glance guide to which Maths Pyramid unit covers which of the Northern Ireland Lines of Development. It should be noted that, as Maths Pyramid is designed to stretch the more able child, the units cover not only level 3 objectives, but also level 4. This will enable you to assess the likely difficulty of the material within each unit as well as its coverage of the Northern Ireland curriculum.

Unit	Topics	Lines of Development
1	Place Value and Ordering	N3.1, N3.2
2	Understanding + and −, Mental Calculation Strategies	N3.3, N3.4, N3.5, N3.9
3	Money and 'real life' problems, making decisions, checking results	N3.15, N4.18, R4.6
4	Measures, including problems	M3.1, M3.2, M3.3, M3.4, M4.1, T4.1
5	Shape and space	S3.1, S3.2, S3.3, S3.4, S3.5, S3.7, S3.9, S3.10, S4.1, S4.2, S4.3
6	Reasoning about shapes	R3.1, R3.2, R3.3, R4.3
7	Counting and properties of number, reasoning about numbers	R4.3
8	Understanding ×, ÷, mental calculation strategies	N3.10, N3.11, N3.12, N3.17, N4.5, N4.9
9	Money and 'real life' problems, making decisions, checking results	N3.13, N3.15, N4,18
10	Fractions	N3.16, N3.18
11	Understanding +, −, time, including problems, making decisions, checking results	N3.4, N3.5
12	Handling data	
13	Place value, ordering, estimating and rounding	N3.2, N4.1
14	Understanding + and −, mental calculation strategies	N3.3, N3.9
15	Money and 'real life' problems, making decisions, checking results	N3.6, N3.8, N3.13, N3.15
16	Measures and time, including problems	M3.1, M3.2, M3.3, M3.4, M3.5, M3.6, T3.1, T3.2
17	Shape and space	S3.1, S3.2, S3.3, S3.9, S3.10, Sp 3.3, Sp 3.6
18	Reasoning about shapes and space	S3.5, S4.1
19	Counting and properties of number, reasoning about numbers	R3.2, R3.3
20	Understanding + and −, mental calculation strategies	N3.5, N3.9
21	Understanding ×, ÷, money and 'real life' problems	N3.6, N3.8, N3.11, N3.13, N3.15, R3.5
22	Fractions	N3.16, N3.18
23	Handling data	HD3.1, HD3.4
24	Place value, ordering and rounding	N3.1, N3.2, N3.7
25	Understanding + and −, mental calculation strategies	N3.4
26	Money and 'real life' problems	N3.15
27	Measures, including problems	M3.1, M3.2, M3.3, M3.4, M3.5, M3.6, T3.5
28	Shape and space	S3.1, S3.2, S3.3, S3.7, S3.9, Sp3.2, Sp3.3, Sp3.4, Sp3.7, Sp4.7
29	Reasoning	R3.3, R3.4, R3.5
30	Counting and properties of number, reasoning about numbers	N3.10, R3.1, R3.2, R4.3
31	Understanding ×, ÷, mental calculation strategies	N3.22, R3.5, R3.6
32	Money and 'real life' problems, making decisions, checking results	N3.15
33	Fractions	N3.16
34	Understanding + and −, paper and pencil procedures and problems, including time	N3.4
35	Data	

Scotland 5–14 Guidelines

The following chart enables you to select the appropriate Maths Pyramid unit to extend work on the various parts of the Scottish 5–14 Curriculum for Mathematics Levels C and D.

Information Handling

Strand	Level C	Unit	Level D	Unit
Collect	By obtaining information for a task from a variety of given sources, including a simple questionnaire with yes/no type responses; By conducting a survey which extends beyond the class.	12, 23, 35	By selecting sources of information for tasks, including a questionnaire which allows several responses to each question.	
Organise	By using a tally sheet with grouped tallies; By entering data in a table using row and column headings; By using a database where the teacher defines the headings or fields; With the aid, where appropriate of a computer package.	35	By using diagrams or tables; By using a database or spreadsheet table with up to three fields, defined by pupils; With the aid, where appropriate, of a computer package.	12, 23, 35
Display	By constructing a table or chart; By constructing a bar graph with axes graduated in multiple units and discrete categories of information; With the aid, where appropriate, of a computer package.	35	By constructing graphs (bar, line, frequency polygon) and pie charts; – involving simple fractions or decimals; – involving continuous data which has been grouped; With the aid, where appropriate, of a computer package.	
Interpret	From displays and databases: – by retrieving specific records; – by identifying the most and least frequent items; With the aid, where appropriate, of a computer package.	23, 35	From a range of displays and databases by retrieving information subject to one condition.	23, 35

Number, Money and Measurement

Strand	Level C	Unit	Level D	Unit
Range and type of numbers	Work with: – whole numbers up to 1000 (count, order, read/write); – thirds, fifths, eighths, tenths and simple equivalences such as one half = two quarters (practical applications only); – decimals to two places when reading/recording money, and using calculator displays.	1, 10, 13, 22, 24, 33	Work with: – whole numbers up to 1 000 000 (count, order, read/write); – whole numbers up to a million (read/write only); – fractions (all previous plus twentieths, fiftieths, hundredths) and equivalences among these and decimals (in applications); – percentages, decimals to 2 places and equivalences among these in applications in money and measurement.	
Money	Use coins/notes to £5 worth or more, including exchange.	3, 9, 14, 15, 21, 26, 32	Use all UK coins/notes to £20 worth or more, including exchange.	
Add and subtract	Add and subtract: – mentally for one digit to or from whole numbers up to 3 digits; beyond in some cases involving multiples of 10;	2, 14, 20, 25, 26, 34	Add and subtract: – mentally for 2 digit whole numbers, beyond in some cases, involving multiples of 10 or 100;	

Number, Money and Measurement

Strand	Level C	Unit	Level D	Unit
	– mentally for subtraction by "adding on"; – without a calculator for whole numbers with 2 digits, added to or subtracted from 3 digits; – with a calculator for 3-digit whole numbers in applications in number, measurement and money to £20.		– without a calculator, for 4 digits with at most two decimal places (easy examples only); – with a calculator, for 4 digits with at most 2 decimal places; in applications in number, measurement and money.	
Multiply and divide	Multiply and divide: – mentally within the confines of all tables to 10; – mentally for any 2 or 3 digit whole number by 10; – without a calculator for 2 digit whole numbers by any single digit whole number; – with a calculator for 2 or 3 digit whole numbers by a whole number with 1 or 2 digits; in applications in number, measurement and money to £20.	3, 6, 7, 8, 15	Multiply and divide: – mentally for whole numbers by single digits: easy examples only; – mentally for 4 digit numbers including decimals by 10 or 100; – without a calculator for 4 digits with at most 2 decimal places by a single digit; – with a calculator for 4 digits with at most 2 decimal places by a whole number with 2 digits, in applications in number, measurement and money.	8
Round numbers	Round 3 digit whole numbers to the nearest ten (e.g. when estimating).	24	Round any number to the nearest appropriate whole number, ten or hundred.	8
Fractions, percentages and ratio	Find simple fractions ($\frac{1}{3}, \frac{1}{5}, \frac{1}{10}$) of quantities involving 1 or 2 digit numbers.	10, 22, 33	Work with fractions and percentages: – find simple fractions ($\frac{1}{7}, \frac{3}{4}, \frac{3}{5}, \frac{60}{100}$) of quantities involving at most 4 digits (easy examples only).	10, 33
Patterns and sequences	Work with patterns and relationships: – within and among multiplication tables.	1, 2, 6, 7, 19, 29	Continue and describe more complex sequences:	30
Functions and equations	Use a simple "function machine" for operations: – involving doubling, halving, adding and subtracting.	31	Recognise and explain simple relationships: – between two sets of numbers or objects.	
Measure and estimate	Measure in standard units: – weight: accuracy extended to include 20 g weights; 1 kg = 100 g – volume: litre, $\frac{1}{2}$ litre, $\frac{1}{4}$ litre; – area: shapes composed of rectangles/squares or irregular shapes using tiles or grids in square centimetres and metres; Estimate length and height in easily handled standard units: m, $\frac{1}{2}$ m, $\frac{1}{10}$m, cm Select appropriate measuring devices and units for length; Read scales on measuring devices to the nearest graduation where the value of an intermediate graduation may need to be deduced;	4, 16, 27	Measure in standard units: – length: small lengths in millimetres; large lengths like buildings in metres; – weight: extended range of articles, for example own weight; – volume: accuracy extended to small containers in millilitres; 1l = 1000ml; – area: right-angled triangles on cm squared grids; – temperature; Estimate small weights, small areas, small volumes in easily handled standard units; Recognise when kilometres are appropriate; Select appropriate measuring devices and units for weight; Be aware of common Imperial units in appropriate practical applications.	4, 16
Time	Work with time: – use 12 hour times for simple timetables; – conventions for recording time; – work with hours, minutes; – use calendars.	4, 11, 16, 27, 34	Work with time: – use 24 – hour times and equate with 12-hour times; – calculate duration in hours/minutes, mentally if possible; – time activities in seconds with a stopwatch; – calculate speeds (practical activities only).	4, 11, 16, 27, 34

Shape, position and movement

Strand	Level C	Unit	Level D	Unit
Range of shapes	Collect, discuss, make and use 3D and 2D shapes: – identify 2D shapes within 3D shapes; – draw circles using a variety of methods; – recognise 3D shapes from 2D drawings.	28	Collect, discuss, make and use 3D and 2D shapes: – discuss 3D and 2D shapes referring to faces, edges, vertices, diagonals, sides, angles; – recognise pentagon, hexagon; – identify and name equilateral and isosceles triangles; – extend shape vocabulary to radius, diameter, circumference; – create or copy a tiling using a shape template; – make 3D models, solid or skeletal, including using nets: cube and cuboid only; – use the rigidity property of triangles in model-making.	5, 17, 28
Position and movement	Discuss position and movement: – describe the main features of a familiar journey or route; – create paths on squared paper described by instructions such as "forward 5, right 90, forward 7, left 90".	28	Discuss position and movement: – give directions for a route or journey; – use an 8 point compass rose; – use a co-ordinate system to locate a point on a grid; – create patterns by rotating a shape.	28
Symmetry	Work with symmetry: – find lines of symmetry of shapes drawn of squared grids; – complete the missing half of a simple symmetrical shape or pattern on a squared grid.	5, 18	Work with symmetry: – identify and draw lines of symmetry, generally up to 4; – create symmetrical shapes.	5, 6, 18
Angle	Angles: – know that a right angle is 90°; – use "right, acute, obtuse" to describe angles; – know that a straight angle is 180°.	17	Angles: – draw, copy and measure angles accurately within 5 degrees; – use standard notation, 060°, 150°, 300°, to express bearings.	

Answers to Pupil's Book questions

Page 1
1. 942, 881, 818 , 492, 429, 354, 345, 249, 210, 201, 191, 119, 109
2. 1976, 1539, 1060, 967, 661, 616, 540, 410, 401, 358, 224

1a. nine hundred and forty-two
2a. one thousand nine hundred and seventy-six

3. 99, 109, 126, 162, 168, 201, 261, 191, 422, 618, 681, 861
4. 127, 251, 281, 406, 505, 617, 670, 671, 763, 896, 954, 4371, 6070

3a. ninety-nine
4a. one hundred and twenty-seven

🔑 six thousand and seventy

Page 2
Most flowers:
    Snail A
    27 + 32 + 35 + 22 + 16 = 132
Fewest flowers:
    Snail B
    10 + 14 + 12 + 20 = 56

Page 4
1–3. Answers will vary
4. 3 cheeseburgers, 50p change would buy cola, ice cream, salad, chips or a choc bar.

🔑 £18.50

Page 5

1.
1 fish burger	£1.50
1 chips	50p
1 cola	45p
Total	£2.45

2.
1 salad	50p
1 cola	45p
1 choc bar	25p
1 chips	50p
Total	£1.70

3.
2 plain burgers	£2.40
2 chips	£1.00
2 colas	90p
Total	£4.30

4.
1 salad	50p
1 triple burger	£1.75
1 chips	50p
1 choc bar	25p
Total	£3.00

5.
3 cheeseburgers	£4.50
2 chips	£1.00
2 colas	90p
2 ice creams	80p
Total	£7.20

6.
1 fish burger	£1.50
1 chips	50p
1 salad	50p
1 ice cream	40p
1 choc bar	25p
1 cola	45p
Total	£3.60

Page 6

3 × 3 pinboard: 4 ☐ + 1 ☐ + 1 ◇ = 6 possible squares

4 × 4 pinboard: 9 ☐ + 4 ☐ + 4 ◇ + 1 + 1 + 1 = 20 possible squares

5 × 5 pinboard: 16 ☐ + 9 ☐ + 9 ◇ + 4 + 1 + 1 + 4 + 4 + 1 + 1 = 50 possible squares

3 × 3 pinboard: 4 △ + 8 + 8 + 16 + 4 + 4 + 4 + 8 + 8 + 4 + 8 = 76 possible triangles

Page 7
1– 9. Answers will vary

Page 8
(Answers in this order: top right, bottom left, bottom right)
1. 15, 16, 17
2. 11, 12, 13
3. 30, 28, 33
4. 36, 34, 41
5. 30, 32, 44
6. 33, 36, 42

Page 9
$15 + 3 + 20 + 2 = 40$
$16 + 5 + 12 + 7 = 40$
$8 + 14 + 6 + 12 = 40$
$22 + 3 + 0 + 15 = 40$
$15 + 9 + 3 + 13 = 40$
$3 + 13 + 6 + 18 = 40$

 Smallest possible 2×2 total
$15 + 3 + 9 + 6 = 33$
Largest possible 2×2 total
$2 + 28 + 9 + 30 = 69$

Page 10
Answers will vary

Page 11
Answers will vary

Page 12
1. $\frac{3}{4}$
2. $\frac{2}{6}$ or $\frac{1}{3}$
3. $\frac{5}{8}$
4. $\frac{3}{7}$
5. $\frac{1}{5}$
6. $\frac{5}{10}$ or $\frac{1}{2}$
7. $\frac{5}{10}$ or $\frac{1}{2}$
8. $\frac{3}{7}$
9. $\frac{4}{9}$

Page 13
1. 3
2. 10
3. 2
4. 6
5. 4
6. 8
7. 5
8. 8
9. 10
10. 7
11. 4
12. 3
13. 2
14. 5
15. 9
16. 8
17. 3
18. 10
19. 5, 10, 15
20. 1, 2, 3
21. 4, 8, 12
22. 3, 6, 9
23. 2, 4, 6
24. 10, 20, 30

Page 14
1.

	Odd	Not odd
Less than 20	17 3 5 1 19	2 16
20 or more	37 29 41 83 79	28 68 110

2.

	Even	Not even
Less than 30	28 12 10 20 16 4	13 19 17
30 or more	100 88 98 54	63 99 51 37 115

3. Answers will vary

Page 15
832 Eight hundred and thirty-two
273 Two hundred and seventy-three
697 Six hundred and ninety-seven
104 One hundred and four
1703 One thousand seven hundred and three
956 Nine hundred and fifty-six
402 Four hundred and two
518 Five hundred and eighteen
888 Eight hundred and eighty-eight
1414 One thousand four hundred and fourteen
199 One hundred and ninety-nine
1864 One thousand eight hundred and sixty-four
1929 One thousand nine hundred and twenty-nine

nine hundred and sixty-two 962
one thousand three hundred and forty-one 1341
five hundred and sixty-five 565
ninety-nine 99
one thousand nine hundred and nineteen 1919
eight hundred and seventy-five 875
four hundred and thirty-two 432
one thousand and eleven 1011
two hundred and forty-six 246
one hundred and fifty-two 152

3a. 1929, 1864, 1703, 1414, 956, 888, 832, 697, 518, 402, 273, 199, 104
  b. 1919, 1341, 1011, 962, 875, 565, 432, 246, 152, 99

 99, 104, 152, 199, 246, 273, 402, 432, 518, 565, 697, 832, 875, 888, 956, 962, 1011, 1414, 1341, 1703, 1864, 1919, 1929

Page 16
Zig £5.79
Zag £8.87
Zog £9.05

Zig chooses the cheapest route, Zog chooses the most expensive.

 They spend £23.71 altogether

Page 17
1–8. Many possible answers

 £7.80

Page 18
To the nearest half centimetre:
1. $2\frac{1}{2}$ cm
2. 12 cm
3. $2\frac{1}{2}$ cm
4. 5 cm
5. 5 cm
6. 7 cm
7. $3\frac{1}{2}$ cm
8. 2 cm
9. $6\frac{1}{2}$ cm

 Side walls and slopes of roof all measure 2 cm to the nearest half centimetre.

Page 19
1. 1 ℓ 300 mℓ
2. 1 ℓ 200 mℓ
3. 700 mℓ
4. 1 ℓ 200 mℓ
5. 1 ℓ
6. 900 mℓ

Page 21
24 sticks:

5 squares

6 squares

3 squares

Other possibilities:

2 squares

14 squares

15 sticks:

2 large and 2 small squares

Page 23
Largest number of stamps for
£2.00 : 20 × 10p
Three of each kind : £1.95
Five of each kind : £3.25
Ten of each kind : £6.50

Page 24
1. $30p + 30p = 60p$
   $£1.54 − 60p = 94p$ left
2. $£1.00 + 30p + 30p = £1.60$
   $£2.00 − £1.60 = 40p$ left
3. $£1.00 + £1.00 + 50p + 50p + 10p + 5p = £3.25$
   $£5.00 − £3.25 = £1.75$ left
4. $£1.00 + 5p = £1.05$
   $£3.75 − £1.05 = £2.70$ left
5. $50p + 50p + 30p + 5p = £1.35$
   $£2.60 − £1.35 = £1.25$ left
6. $30p + 30p + 30p+ 30p+ 30p + 50p + 10p +10p + 5p + 5p = £2.30$
   $£4.00 − £2.30 = £1.70$

 Answers will vary.

Page 25

1. $\frac{1}{2} = \frac{2}{4} = \frac{3}{6} = \frac{5}{10} = \frac{4}{8}$
2. $\frac{1}{4} = \frac{2}{8} = \frac{3}{12} = \frac{5}{20}$
3. $\frac{1}{8}, \frac{1}{4}, \frac{1}{3}, \frac{3}{8}, \frac{1}{2}, \frac{5}{8}, \frac{3}{4}, \frac{7}{8}$
4. 10   9   8   15   25   250
5. 1   2   3   4   10   20
6. 3   15   27   18   54   75
7. £1.50, 75p   £2.50, £1.25
   £4.00, £2.00   £40.00, £20.00
   £1.00, 50p   £12.50, £6.25
   £300.00, £150.00   £400.00, £200.00

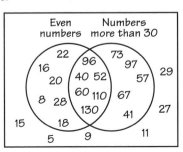 £2.25   £3.75   £6.00   £60.00

   £1.50   18.75   £450.00   £600.00

Page 26

1. 12   24   18   10   14   22   16
2. 8   2   6   4   3   5   1

3. Plain cake
   Double:
   200 g sugar
   200 g margarine
   4 eggs
   300 g flour
   2 teaspoons vanilla essence

   Half:
   50 g sugar
   50 g margarine
   1 egg
   75 g flour
   $\frac{1}{2}$ teaspoon vanilla essence

   Chocolate cake
   Double :
   60 g ground almonds
   180 g plain flour
   240 g caster sugar
   4 egg yolks
   4 tablespoons milk
   200 g chocolate
   100 g butter
   100 g walnuts
   400 ml cream

   Half:
   15 g ground almonds
   45 g plain flour
   60 g caster sugar
   1 egg yolk
   1 tablespoon milk
   50 g chocolate
   25 g butter
   25 g walnuts
   100 ml cream

Page 27

1.

	Multiple of 3	Not a Multiple of 3
More than 30	96 57 60	40 52 110 73 130 67 41 97
Not more than 30	15 9 18 27	8 16 22 11 5 28 29 20

Even numbers / Numbers more than 30 (Venn diagram):
22, 16, 20, 8, 28, 15, 18, 5 (even numbers)
96, 40, 52, 60, 110, 130, 9 (overlap)
73, 97, 57, 67, 41, 29, 27, 11 (more than 30)

3. Answers will vary

Page 28

1. 101, 109, 110, 151, 242, 375, 489, 555, 626, 631, 713, 818, 881, 982, 1000, 1010
2. 191, 222, 263, 354, 396, 427, 501, 521, 542, 635, 653, 706, 728, 892, 900, 1019
3. 1010, 1001, 1000, 967, 843, 726, 672, 626, 500, 421, 401, 398, 181, 142, 141
4. 153, 217, 264, 290, 460, 493, 507, 616, 784, 873, 939, 961, 1013, 1039, 2063, 6020
5. 61, 65, 69, 73, 77, 81, 85, 89
   15, 20, 25, 30, 35, 40, 45, 50
   71, 76, 81, 86, 91, 96, 101, 106
   278, 276, 274, 272, 270, 268, 266
   384, 389, 394, 399, 404, 409, 414

Page 29

1. 85
2. 720
3. 886
4. 645
5. 137
6. 375
7. 151
8. 258

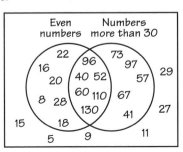

1. 90 → 90
   81 → 80
   97 → 100
   85 → 90
2. 724 → 720
   720 → 720
   729 → 730
   730 → 730
3. 888 → 890
   886 → 890
   892 → 890
   882 → 880
4. 647 → 650
   653 → 650
   611 → 610
   645 → 650
5. 139 → 140
   137 → 140
   131 → 130
   145 → 150
6. 371 → 370
   375 → 380
   362 → 360
   379 → 380
7. 154 → 150
   151 → 150
   159 → 160
   160 → 160
8. 263 → 260
   253 → 250
   258 → 260
   269 → 270

Page 30

1. 700
2. 430
3. 520
4. 180
5. 230
6. 650
7. 960
8. 870

Page 31

Many possible answers.

Page 32

1–10. Many possible answers.

Page 33

1. 1 sausage 70p
   1 large chips £1.00
   1 peas 55p
   2 small ice creams £1.20
   Total £3.45

2. 2 large fish £3.00
   2 large chips £2.00
   2 fizzy drinks £2.00
   Total £7.00

3. 2 fish fingers £1.50
   2 small chips £1.20
   2 fizzy drinks £2.00
   Total £4.70

4. 2 large fish £3.00
   1 fish fingers 75p
   2 large chips £2.00
   1 large ice cream 80p
   Total £6.55

5. 1 burger 75p
   1 small chips 60p
   1 peas 55p
   1 fizzy drink £1.00
   Total £2.90

6. 2 large chips £2.00
   2 large ice creams £1.60
   2 orange juices £1.20
   Total £4.80

Page 34

1. 35 cm + 52 cm + 1 m + 79 cm + 20 cm
   = 2 m 86 cm
2. 80 cm × 6 = 4 m 80 cm
   6 m − 4 m 80 cm = 1 m 20 cm
   1 m 20 cm left
3. 4 × 50 g = 200 g
           Nell's collection weighs 200 g.
   500 g ÷ 50 g = 10
   10 − 4 = 6
       Her brother gave her six more books.
4. 500 m × 7 = 3500 m
       Tiffany swims 3 km 500 m a week.
5. 125 g + 50 g + 75 g + 50 g +
   50 g = 350 g.
       Total weight of the sweets 350g.
   350 g ÷ 2 = 175 g   175 g left.
6. 500 ml ÷ 5 = 100
           100 spoonfuls in the bottle.
   100 ÷ 2 = 50
           The bottle will last 50 days.
7. It is 9 months until her next birthday.
           She will be 2 years old.
8. 18 × 2 = 36
           Marcus will need 36 jugs.

Page 35

66 cubes needed to build a model with 6 floors.

91 needed to build 7 floors

190 needed to build 10 floors

Each successive floor needs the same number of cubes as the one before, plus four more.

Page 36

1. woods
2. rocks
3. rocks
4. lake

5. NE
6. W
7. NW
8. SW
9. NE

10. A9
11. E8
12. G5
13. F3
14. C7, C8, D7, D8, D2, E2, F2
15. E4

Page 39

1. a = 47
    b = 14
    c = 10
    d = 16
    e = 26
    f = 46
    g = 22
    h = 41

2. a = 10
    b = 15
    c = 25
    d = 50
    e = 20
    f = 30
    g = 35
    h = 40

3. a = 21
    b = 30
    c = 24
    d = 36
    e = 9
    f = 12
    g = 18
    h = 15

4. a = 70
    b = 100
    c = 40
    d = 80
    e = 30
    f = 90
    g = 50
    h = 60

5. a = 24
    b = 40
    c = 140
    d = 124
    e = 100
    f = 64
    g = 98
    h = 80

Page 41

Many possible answers.

Page 42

1. £1.00 + 15p + 70p + 29p + £3.40 + 92p + 10p = £6.56
2. £5.50 + 55p + £5.10 + £3.10 + 35p + 10p + 25p + £1.05 = £16.00
3. £2.00 + 10p + £5.00 + 5p + 75p + 50p + 50p + 20p = £9.10
4. 43p + £10.00 + 60p + £5.00 + 28p + 16p + £2.00 +7p = £18.54
5. £1.60 + 9p + 40p + 26p + 16p + 10p + 7p + 20p + £1.20 = £4.08

Page 45

1. 40 minutes
2. 1 hour 50 minutes
3. 30 minutes
4. 1 hour 10 minutes
5. 1 hour
6. 10 minutes
7. 1 hour
8. Answers will vary.

Page 46

1. 15
2. 700 mℓ
3. 34
4. 18 weeks
5. 66
6. 105, 150
7. 8:35 a.m.
8. 200 jugfuls, 3 hours 20 minutes, 20 past 2